ATOMIC ABSORPTION SPECTROSCOPY

ATOMIC ABSORPTION SPECTROSCOPY

JAMES W. ROBINSON

Department of Chemistry
Louisiana State University
Baton Rouge, Louisiana

1966

MARCEL DEKKER, Inc., New York

Rupl. acc. # 733

First Printing: July 1966

Second Printing: March 1967

To Mrs. Winnie

Preface

The problem of writing a book to cover any given subject completely is always hindered by the fact that, between the time of writing and publishing, significant research work is reported, and inclusion of such work becomes an almost impossible task. This problem is particularly acute in the fast-moving field of atomic absorption spectroscopy. The type of presentation given in this book may be compared to a "still" shot from a moving picture, which is only accurate for an instant of time.

As a result, emphasis has been given to the basic principles of the subject and to the application of those principles. It is hoped that, by using this work, the reader will be able to understand current views on the subject and to assess the value of new innovations as they appear.

Specific attention has been paid to fundamentals such as the formation of free atoms and the absorption of radiation by these atoms. The functioning of equipment, including all components, is discussed from the standpoint of the analytical chemist.

The application of atomic absorption spectroscopy is covered in two chapters. The parameters which must be controlled in order to get reproducible results are discussed in Chapter 3. In Chapter 4, a concise record has been made for each element of the experimental conditions which have been reported as giving satisfactory analytical results. Finally, a chapter on atomic fluorescence was added (Chapter 5) because so much of the subject matter of atomic absorption applies directly to atomic fluorescence.

With the broad approach taken to the subject of atomic absorption, it is hoped that the book will be useful to three groups of people: the graduate student in analytical chemistry, the research chemist who wishes to know "if" and "how" the method is applicable to solving his problem, and the analytical chemist responsible for providing rapid and accurate analyses for research and industrial problems.

The author is indebted to many people for help and suggestions in writing this book. In particular, Walter Slavin, of Perkin-Elmer Corp., and Dick Reiss, of Aztec Instruments, have been most helpful. Finally, after collecting and categorizing so much information concerning this field, it became abundantly obvious that fitting tribute should be paid to Alan Walsh and his co-workers at the C.S.I.R.O., Australia, who first presented this analytical field and then developed so many of the significant contributions to its progress.

J. W. R.

Louisiana State University
Baton Rouge, Louisiana
May, 1966

Contents

CHAPTER ONE

Introduction

I. WHAT IS ATOMIC-ABSORPTION SPECTROSCOPY?

Atomic-absorption spectroscopy is the study of absorption of radiant energy by atoms. As an analytical process, it includes the conversion of combined elements to atoms, and the absorption of radiant energy by those atoms. The conversion of elements from chemical compounds to their atomic state involves physics, chemistry, and voodoo, the

latter playing the most important role; the absorption of
energy by these atoms, however, involves only physics and
appears to be a predictable and measurable property of the
atom. The radiant energy absorbed is in the form of very
narrow absorption lines, generally in the visible and ultraviolet spectral regions. During its absorption, outer valence
electrons are excited.

There is a simple relationship between atomic-absorption
and emission spectroscopy. This relationship is illustrated
in Figure 1.1, which shows an excited atom in equilibrium

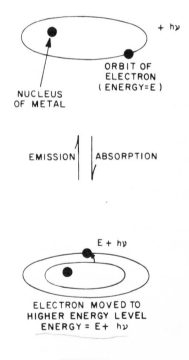

FIGURE 1.1

The Relationship between Atomic-Absorption and Atomic-
Emission Spectroscopy.

with an unexcited atom and a photon. The formation of the ground-state atom plus a photon from an excited atom is the basis of emission spectrography; the reverse process is the basis of atomic-absorption spectroscopy.

This simple illustration reveals to us the gross effect of variables on the system. For example, any change that increases the total population of atoms obtained from a given sample will increase both emission and absorption signals. The use of highly combustible solvents, organometallic compounds, and improved combustion all tend to increase the total atom population and therefore increase both the emission and absorption signals. In contrast, an increase in flame temperature alone increases the number of excited atoms and therefore the *thermal* emission signal. For a constant atom population, the number of unexcited atoms must decrease (albeit very slightly); hence the absorption signal should also decrease. Similarly, conditions which would preserve the life of unexcited atoms, for example, a reducing flame, would enhance the absorption signal significantly, but would have only a secondary effect on the emission signal.

An examination of the mathematical relationships governing emission and absorption gives us a more fundamental understanding of the two fields.

The intensity S of a thermal emission line is given by

$$S = \frac{N_2 E}{\tau} = \frac{N_1 E}{\tau} \frac{g_1}{g_2} e^{-E/kT} \tag{1.1}$$

$$E = h\nu \tag{1.2}$$

where S = intensity of the emission line
N_2 = number of excited atoms
N_1 = number of unexcited atoms
τ = lifetime of an excited atom
E = energy of excitation

g_1/g_2 = a priori probability of the ratio of atoms in the ground
state and the excited state

T = temperature

k = Boltzman distribution

h = Planck's constant

ν = frequency of the emission line = c/λ

c = speed of light

λ = wavelength of the emission line or the excitation
wavelength

It can be seen that the intensity of the emission line is proportional to the number of excited atoms. Also, for a given number of atoms, the number of excited atoms is a function of the temperature T and the frequency of the emission line ν. With an increase in T, there is a corresponding increase in N_2, the number of excited atoms. For a constant temperature and as E, the required energy for excitation, is increased, there is a decrease in N_2, and hence a decrease in the intensity of emission.

The important point is that the intensity of an emission line is controlled by the number of excited atoms, which in turn is a function the wavelength of emission and the tem-

TABLE 1.1

THE RELATIONSHIP BETWEEN THE TEMPERATURE, EXCITATION
WAVELENGTH, AND THE NUMBER OF EXCITED ATOMS,
IN A GIVEN ATOM POPULATION

Excitation wavelength, A	Number of excited atoms per unit population at		Enhancement caused by 500°K temperature increase
	3000°K	3500°K	
2000	10^{-10}	$10^{-8.6}$	30
3000	$10^{-6.7}$	$10^{-5.7}$	9
6000	$10^{-3.3}$	$10^{-3.0}$	2.3

perature of the system. This is illustrated by Table 1.1, which shows the number of thermally excited atoms calculated for various temperatures and wavelengths. Note, only a small fraction of the atoms is excited even when the excitation energy is low and the temperature is high.

In contrast to this, the degree of absorption follows the relationship

$$\int K_\nu d_\nu = \frac{\pi e^2}{mc} N_1 f \tag{1.3}$$

where K = absorption coefficient at frequency ν
e = charge on an electron
m = mass of the electron
c = speed of light
f = oscillator strength of the absorbing line

$$f = \frac{\lambda_0^2 g_2}{8\pi g_1} N_1 A_2{}^1 \tag{1.4}$$

where ν_0 = wavelength of resonance line
A_1^2 = Einstein's coefficient of spontaneous emission

The only variable is N_1, the number of atoms available to absorb. The Beer-Lambert law is

$$I_1 = I_0 e^{-kbc} \tag{1.5}$$

and cannot be applied directly to atomic-absorption spectroscopy. We seldom have a system of atoms in a steady state of homogeneous distribution, and it is therefore impossible to ascribe any valid number to c or b. However, the principles of the law must apply in that the intensity of unabsorbed light is a function of the negative log of the absorption coefficient. This enables us to plot calibration curves and relate concentration and absorption.

It will be noted again that the degree of absorption is a

function of the oscillator strength and is almost independent of all variables other than the number of atoms in the system. Further, it can be seen that absorption is carried out by the unexcited atoms.

To summarize, the physics of atomic absorption has the following inherent advantages over atomic emission:

1. Atomic absorption is almost independent of temperature and the absorption wavelength.

2. The bulk of the atom population is unexcited and can absorb, but only the small excited fraction can emit.

3. In atomic absorption it is sufficient to measure the ratio I_1/I_0. In emission, the absolute value of the emission signal must be determined.

It should be noted at this point that, when flame atomizers are used, changes in flame temperature can affect the efficiency of producing atoms from a given sample. This directly controls N_1, the number of unexcited atoms in the light path. Such a temperature effect on atomic absorption can be readily observed experimentally. However, this should not be confused with the effect of temperature on the physics of the absorption process by each atom; this is negligible in extent.

To give an over-all view of atomic absorption, the advantages and disadvantages are briefly listed at this point and are discussed in more detail in other sections of the book.

II. THE ADVANTAGES OF ATOMIC-ABSORPTION SPECTROSCOPY

A. Sensitivity

The procedure is highly sensitive. Many elements can be determined at the part-per-million level or less. In this respect it is at least competitive with any other analytical procedure used for elemental analysis.

B. Accuracy and Precision

With the help of calibration curves, high precision and accuracy are obtainable. The task of making valid calibration curves is easier than in most other analytical procedures, because the absorption signal is considerably free of interference. The tedious process of compensation for possible interfering compounds is reduced. Representative standard solutions can therefore be made up without difficulty.

C. Few Interferences

The two types of interference most commonly encountered are spectral and chemical. Direct spectral interference is the absorption by materials other than the sample element. Since metals absorb at well-defined wavelengths and over very narrow bandwidths, absorption interference by atoms of other elements is rare. So narrow are the absorption bands that isotopes of the same element will not absorb each other's radiation. Advantage has been taken of this to determine the isotope content of lithium and uranium. It will be noted that most elements emit radiation identical in wavelength to that at which they absorb. This is particularly important at the longer wavelengths (>3000 A), where emission intensities may be high. Unless it is eliminated, this emission signal is registered by the detector and causes an apparent change in the absorption signal which may be mistaken for an interelement interference.

To avoid this source of error, it is essential to prevent the flame-emission signal from being detected. This can be done by modulation of the light source and the detector. Failure to modulate allows emission from the flame to remain a constant source of error and makes difficult the use of this phenomenon as a quantitative analytical tool. It will be discussed at greater length in Chapter 2, Section II.

A second type of spectral interference arises from absorption of the light signal by molecules, or by fragments of molecules, in the optical path. This is particularly apparent when a flame is used as an atomizer. It has been found that absorption takes place by unburned hydrogen, by OH moieties, and by the products of combustion of organic solvents. This can be particularly bad when long-path flame adapters are used, in which case more than 80 per cent of the signal may be absorbed by the combustion products. This problem can be controlled somewhat by controlling flame conditions and, if possible, by choosing an absorption wavelength at which the effect is small.

Chemical interference arises from the difficulty of producing neutral metal atoms from the metal compounds or ions in the original sample. The ease of this step is affected by the anion combined with the sample element; for example, $Ca_3(PO_4)_2$ is harder to break down than $CaCl_2$. Some progress has been made in eliminating this problem by using EDTA or other complexing organic compounds.

Although these interferences may at first glance seem to be extensive, they are more easily controlled and are less extensive than those encountered in emission processes.

D. Simplicity

Commercial equipment is comparatively simple to operate. Very little training is required to manipulate the instrument. Although basic research in the fundamentals of the phenomenon itself may be far from simple, routine analytical results can be obtained with a minimum of training on the part of the operator. This is in contrast to other analytical techniques such as activation analysis or X-ray fluorescence.

E. Cost

Of paramount importance is the cost of equipment. The most expensive complete model is priced at about $7000. Of course, cheaper models are available, but these are generally less elegant or are capable of only a limited performance. In these days of astronomical costs for instrumentation, it is a relief to see an exception to the trend.

III. THE DISADVANTAGES OF ATOMIC-ABSORPTION SPECTROSCOPY

All analytical techniques are limited in some respects. Atomic absorption is no exception. The most notable of these limitations are listed below.

A. Limited Application

About 45 elements (excluding the rare earths) have been detected by this method. Methods have not yet been developed for detecting nonmetals and some metalloids. In many cases this is because their absorption lines are in the vacuum ultraviolet, and present-day equipment, which is open to the atmosphere and uses flame atomizers, cannot be used in this spectral region. Also no effort has been made to develop light sources for nonmetals.

B. Flame Atomizers: Oxide Formation

Commercial equipment uses flame atomizers, which, for many samples, are satisfactory and cheap; however, it limits the sample type to liquids. Further, some metals form stable oxides in flames. A serious loss in neutral-atom population results with a corresponding loss in sensitivity. Progress has been made in overcoming this problem by controlling flame conditions, but it seems to be a paradox to use a flame as a reducing medium. Surely the use of flame atomizers is one of the blind spots of commercial equipment.

C. Simultaneous Analysis

At present, simultaneous analysis of several metals in one sample (as in emission spectrography) is not possible on most equipment. This can be a limitation, particularly when only a small sample is available. Equipment for multielement analysis is available, but its use is not widespread.

D. Interferences

Although the procedure is remarkably free of interferences, some have been noted from anions. For any given cation, different anions form compounds with different stabilities. This directly affects the production of neutral atoms in the reduction step.

E. Conclusions

Although numerous disadvantages have been noted, the simplicity, convenience, and broad application of the technique make it an attractive feature in most analytical laboratories.

CHAPTER TWO

Equipment

Basically, atomic-absorption equipment is similar to other spectroscopic instrumentation. There is a radiant-energy source, a sample cell, a monochromator, and a detector. A schematic diagram of the equipment used is shown in Figure 2.1.

In a single-beam instrument a steady source of radiant energy traverses the atomizer and falls on the monochromator. Light with the pertinent wavelength is first separated

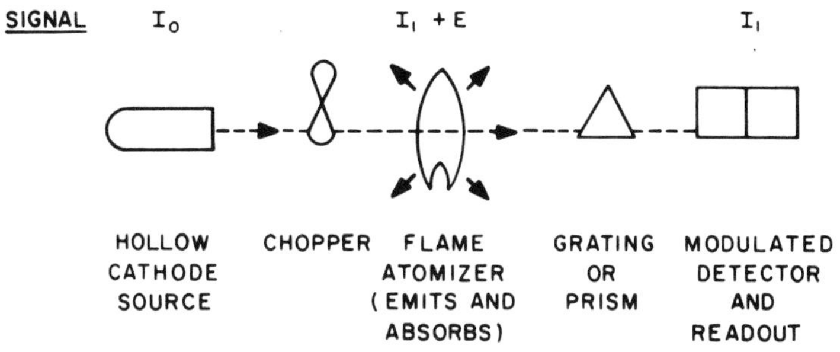

SIGNAL I_0 $I_1 + E$ I_1

HOLLOW	CHOPPER	FLAME	GRATING	MODULATED
CATHODE		ATOMIZER	OR	DETECTOR
SOURCE		(EMITS AND	PRISM	AND
		ABSORBS)		READOUT

FIGURE 2.1

Schematic Diagram of a Single-Beam Atomic-Absorption Instrument.

by the monochromator from other radiation emitted from the source and then falls on the detector. The output from the detector is amplified and registered on the readout system. Any absorption by the sample is measured as the difference between the intensity of unabsorbed radiation I_0 and the intensity of radiation after absorption. If a double-beam instrument is used, the ratio I_1/I_0 is measured. The various components of the equipment are discussed below.

I. RADIATION SOURCES

The most common source of radiation is the hollow cathode. This type is much more successful than continuous sources because of the narrowness of atomic-absorption lines.

The "natural" spectral width of absorption lines is about 10^{-4} A, and this finite width reflects the natural energy spread of the ground and the excited-state levels. The natural line width is broadened by the Doppler effect;

in practice this increases the absorption line width to about 0.01 A. Pressure broadening causes a further increase in line width to about 0.02 A. Pressure broadening may be resonance broadening caused by collision between like atoms or collision with foreign atoms (called Lorenz broadening). Both types of collisions increase the width of the absorption lines. An increase in the temperature increases the broadening effect of all three phenomena. Further, absorption-line widths are dependent on the wavelength of the resonance line. The net result is that the sample may absorb over a spectral bandwidth varying from 0.006 to 0.030 A. Typical wide and narrow absorption-line widths are indicated in Table 2.1.

TABLE 2.1
SPECTRAL WIDTH OF ABSORPTION LINES[a]

	Absorption line width	
Temperature	1000°K	3000°K
Na (5890 A)	0.028 A	0.048 A
Zn (2138 A)	0.006 A	0.01 A

[a] Fundamental width 10^{-4} A; broadened by Doppler effect, temperature, and pressure broadening.

If a continuous source, such as a hydrogen lamp, is used for atomic absorption, only the energy in this narrow absorption wave band can be absorbed. With normal dispersion, light with a spectral band width of roughly 5 A will fall on the detector. If *all* the light in a spectral band of 0.02 A is absorbed, the detector will record a loss of only 0.4 per cent of original signal. For high sensitivity the absorption of 1 per cent of the energy which can be absorbed should be detectable. Suppose a hydrogen-lamp source was used and a spectral band of 5 A fell on the detector. If there was 1 per cent absorption of the resonance line (width 0.02 A), the total energy falling on the detector would only diminish 0.004 per cent, and the detector would register a decrease of the same magnitude. Conventional detectors are not capable of registering so small a change in signal with any reasonable degree of precision. It would therefore be impossible to achieve high sensitivity or even useful quantitative data by using a continuous source under these conditions particularly at shorter wavelengths.

This difficulty was neatly overcome by Walsh (1), who demonstrated that a hollow cathode emitted very narrow spectral lines. If the hollow cathode is made of the same element as the sample, the line width of the source is narrower than the absorption-line width and is therefore completely available for absorption. In addition, since there is usually no unabsorbable background light falling on the detector, the output approaches zero energy when the spectral line is absorbed intensely.

A. Hollow Cathodes

A diagram of the hollow cathode is shown in Figure 2.2. It is based on the design by Jones and Walsh (2). A voltage is applied between the anode and the cathode. Atoms of gas (He or ·A) become charged by the anode and bombard the cathode. Here they impinge on the metal surface, dislodging (or "sputtering") excited metal atoms into the atmosphere. The excited atoms emit light of wavelengths characteristic to the metal. The residual unexcited atoms form a cloud and diffuse either to other walls of the hollow cathode or to the glass wall of the hollow cathode.

This cloud of neutral atoms is detrimental to the performance of the source, particularly if the cathode is hot.

In this case the spectral-line width of the emitted radiation
will be broadened by the Doppler effect. However, the cool
atom cloud will reabsorb some of this energy before it
emerges from the tube. The net result is a decrease in signal
intensity. Moreover, the energy lost is at the center of the

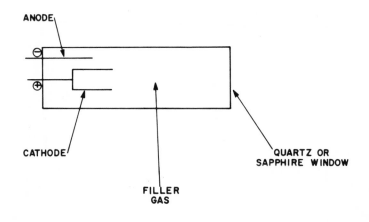

FIGURE 2.2

Schematic Diagram of a Sealed Hollow Cathode.

wavelength range, that is, the most useful energy (Figure
2.3). This problem cannot be completely overcome, but it
can be reduced by operating the cathode at low temperature, which reduces the Doppler broadening. The resultant
emission line may therefore be reduced in intensity but is
not so distorted.

For a single-element hollow cathode, the intensity of the
signal depends on the effectiveness of the bombardment of
the hollow cathode by the charged filler gas, that is, on the
sputtering efficiency. To effect sputtering, the lattice energy
of the metal surface must be overcome by the kintic energy
of the bombarding gas. The lattice energy is a basic prop-

erty of the metal and cannot easily be varied, except by
temperature. For spectral reasons it is better to operate at
low temperature.

However, the kinetic energy of the bombarding gas is
directly controlled by the mass of the gas atoms and the

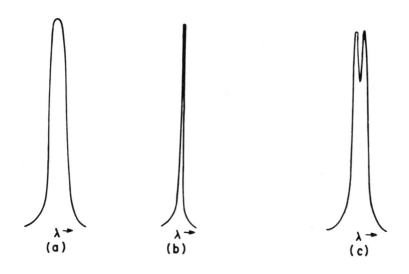

FIGURE 2.3

Distortion of Spectral Line Shape in a Hollow Cathode. (*a*)
Shape of Spectral Line Emitted by a Hollow Cathode. (*b*) Shape
of Spectral Energy Bond Absorbed by Cool Atoms in Hollow
Cathodes. (*c*) Shape of Net Signal Emerging from Hollow
Cathodes.

voltage across the electrodes; this controls the degree of
acceleration of the gas ions. Also, the mean free path of the
gas determines the duration of acceleration. The acceler-
ating voltage and the mean free path control the maximum
kinetic energy of the gas atoms. For successful operation
this must be greater than the lattice energy of the metal.

The geometry of the components of the source is also important. The relative positions of the anode and cathode do not seem to be important, except that they be far enough apart to allow good acceleration of the filler gas. However, the shape of the cathode is important. Ideally, this should be a tube sealed at one end and open at the other. The use of a tubular shape increases the intensity by generating a maximum number of excited atoms in the optical-light path. By sealing the path at one end and reducing the size of the opening at the other, the diffusion of neutral atoms from the cathode to the main body of the source is decreased (*3*). Those atoms which do not diffuse out but redeposit on the inner walls of the cathode are available for sputtering and excitation in future use.

The filler gas is usually an inert gas. Helium and argon have been used extensively and operate satisfactorily, but little use has been made of the other inert gases. However, under the operating conditions of the hollow cathode, each gas emits its characteristic emission spectrum. Occasionally, the frequency of one of these emitted lines may be very similar to the frequency of the metal resonance-absorption line to be used in the analysis. If these two lines are not optically resolved, a loss in analytical sensitivity will result. The problem can usually be solved by using a different filler gas. For example, it has been found by workers at the Perkin-Elmer Corporation (*4*) that lead hollow cathode lamps should use helium filler gas rather than argon.

Lamps filled with helium are usually more intense than lamps filled with argon. However, helium unfortunately "cleans-up" more rapidly than argon, and the life of such a lamp is therefore usually considerably shorter than that of argon lamps. For this reason, commercial lamps are usually made with argon filler gas, unless there is some particular advantage to using neon, as in the case of lead lamps.

1. Multielement Hollow Cathode

Two basic types of multielement hollow cathodes have been used. The first has the same design as the single-element hollow cathode described in Section IA. Cathodes have been made of an alloy, or of several joined strips of different metals. However, a problem was encountered with both designs. One metal was always more volatile than the others and produced a relatively high concentration of that metal in the neutral-atom cloud. On redepositing on the walls of the cathode, an increase in the surface area of this metal resulted. At the same time, the exposed surface of other metals decreased. On continual use, the emission from the volatile metal increased, but the emission from the other metals decreased. A steady drift in the signal from the source was therefore obtained, with some metals increasing and some decreasing. This problem should be greatly reduced by using an ac power supply, but at the time of writing, no experimental evaluation has been reported.

An alternate to this design was developed by Walsh (5). It uses several different cathodes in the same tube, and each cathode is made of a different element (Figure 2.4). This system apparently works satisfactorily but is not available commercially.

Massman (6) and Butler and Strasheim (7) built multi-element lamps by pressing various metals together to form a cathode. The stability of the cathode was improved by arranging the metal rings in the order of their volatility and by choosing an optimum operating current.

Recently Perkin-Elmer Corp. (4) constructed a cathode from a mixture of copper, chromium, cobalt, iron, manganese, and nickel. The powdered metals were pressed together using the techniques of powder metallurgy. These hollow cathodes are now available commercially.

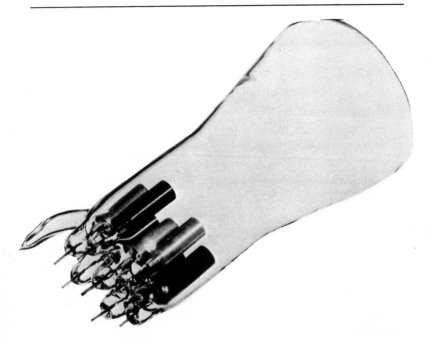

FIGURE 2.4

Multielement Hollow Cathodes [Walsh (5)].

2. Demountable Hollow Cathode

As an alternate to the sealed hollow cathode, an unsealed demountable system was developed by Koirtyohann and Feldman (8). The principle is exactly the same as the sealed source, but as the name implies the hollow cathode can be dismantled. The cathode is made of a metal thimble, such as copper, which has a simple emission spectrum. A second metal in the form of a strip or a chemical salt can be put inside the thimble. No special care or adjustment is needed to do this, provided there is good electrical contact. The filler gas is continuously bled in and evacuated to maintain constant pressure. This type of hollow cathode is particularly useful for laboratories where hollow cathodes made from numerous different metals have to be used.

Demountable hollow cathodes have also been successfully made by Strasheim and Butler (9), who, found that they were dependable as long as the current and voltage were linearly related to each other.

3. High-Intensity Hollow Cathodes

A significant advance has been made by Jones and Walsh on the simple, sealed, hollow cathode described earlier (2). This new radiation source emits resonance lines that are greatly enhanced in intensity. It is illustrated in Figure 2.5. The cathode and the anode are similar in size and shape to those used in the simple hollow cathode. The anode is about half an inch from the cathode. Current flows between the two, and sputtering of the cathode takes place. A cloud of neutral excited metal atoms is produced in the normal fashion.

Two auxiliary cathodes are close to the sputtering cathode. These cathodes are coated with an electron-emissive material, such as alkaline earth carbonates. They are powered independently at a low voltage and produce a high electron density. These electrons pass through the space immediately above the sputtering cathode and interact with the neutral atoms in the metal cloud. The electrons are at a low-energy level; the energy is insufficient to ionize the atoms, but is high enough to excite them. The net result is a great increase in the intensity of all the resonance lines: those that terminate in the ground state.

It has been found in practice that there is an actual depression of the extent of ionization of the free atoms.

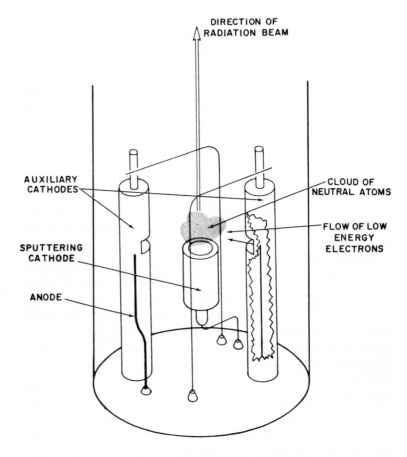

DIRECTION OF
RADIATION BEAM

AUXILIARY
CATHODES

CLOUD OF
NEUTRAL ATOMS

FLOW OF LOW
ENERGY
ELECTRONS

SPUTTERING
CATHODE

ANODE

FIGURE 2.5

Schematic Diagram of High-Intensity Hollow Cathodes.

The effects of the auxiliary "cathodes" are therefore two-fold. First, the resonance lines emitted by the source are greatly brightened, and, second, the unwanted ionization lines are suppressed.

The advantage of these lamps is that their high radiation intensity will allow the detector to operate under quieter electronic conditions with a consequent gain in precision. Also, weak resonance lines will now be more useful for quantitative analytical purposes.

It seems only a matter of time before these lamps are used in the field of atomic fluorescence. Their use should result in significant gains in sensitivity in this new field.

4. Life Limitations

A sealed hollow cathode can be expected to operate for several years under reasonable conditions. However, there are several causes of eventual breakdown. During the course of production, the last traces of air or oxygen are removed by using the anode metal as a "getter." The polarity of the electrodes of the hollow cathode is switched, and clouds of atoms of the anode metal are generated. These react with the last traces of oxygen and remove them. The best getter metals are zirconium, barium, titanium, and tantalum.

New hollow cathodes may not have been cleaned up efficiently in manufacture. This is apparent when the lamp is turned on, because it glows with the typical red-purple color of an electrical discharge in air. The defect can be remedied by reversing the polarity of the electrodes and running the lamp for several hours, until the discharge color becomes that of the filler gas: blue-purple for argon and orange-yellow for neon. Any small leaks that may develop around seals, etc., may be detected and corrected in the same fashion. They should be corrected immediately, since there is a limit to the quantity of air that can be cleaned up this way.

A second limitation is caused by the loss of metal from the hollow cathode. This is particularly bad with low-boiling metals, such as lead or selenium. The currents used with these lamps should always be kept low, otherwise the metal will boil out. Not only does this result in a loss of signal, but the cloud of metal formed diffuses onto the inner glass walls of the source and can electrically short circuit the cathode and anode. This of course results in a complete breakdown but it can be avoided by proper usage. However, even if the hollow cathode is used properly, and there are no air leaks, the cloud of metal atoms leaving the cathode diffuse to the glass walls and trap atoms of filler gas. The internal filler-gas pressure decreases and ultimately becomes too low for the source to operate.

Some attention has been given to sources other than the hollow cathode. These are briefly described below.

B. Discharge Lamps

These are used extensively for some of the very volatile metals, such as sodium or mercury. They are commercially available and present no special problems.

C. Continuous Radiation Sources

Continuous sources, such as hydrogen lamps, have been used with some degree of success. It was noted by Cooke (10) that the absorption signal was low but very stable. The high stability allowed increased amplification and compensated to some extent for the loss of absorption signal. However, further experimental work by Professor Cooke showed that this compensation was insufficient, particularly at shorter wavelengths, thus limiting their application for quantitative work.

D. Flame Radiation Emission Sources

As a qualitative tool, the flame has been used with some measure of success. A flame, as used in a flame photometer, is located on the atomic-absorption instrument at the correct position for the source. A solution of the metal of interest is aspirated into the flame and emission takes place. The lines emitted include the important lines that originate in the ground state of the atom. These are the lines that are absorbed in atomic-absorption spectroscopy. The degree of absorption by a sample is measured in the conventional manner. The advantage of this system is that any metal which emits significantly can be used. Any laboratory therefore finds itself equipped to examine the absorption spectrum of many metals without the expense and delay of buying the hollow cathode. Unfortunately, for quantitative work, a high degree of stability is required in the flame source. It must be remembered that the absorption signal measured is $I_0 - I_1$ and is frequently the difference between two large numbers. Any significant variation in one of the numbers I_0 causes large errors in the difference between the numbers. The emission signal from the flame does not have the required stability, particularly when liquid samples with high metal concentration are used. The flame can therefore be used only for the most approximate quantitative work; it is useful, however, for qualitative and semiquantitative work. Experts in flame photometry will probably challenge this statement, but when they recall the care and skill required to maintain a constant-flame-emission signal for extended periods of time they may be more inclined to agree. The importance of this point becomes more obvious when it is remembered that the great majority of people using atomic absorption will be interested in it as a routine analytical procedure to which the minimum of attention may be devoted.

E. Time-Resolved Spark

An electrical source such as that used in emission spectrography was demonstrated by Strasheim (*11*) as the time-resolved spark. The emission lines from an electrical discharge were used with modification. Under normal conditions the intensity of these emission lines varies with time. Further, the spectral width of each line is significant. Each property is very undesirable for atomic absorption. These problems are alleviated by using a time-resolved spark. The basis is as follows. When discharge ceases, the emission signal persists for a short period. During this period, the lines become rapidly narrower and less intense. Doppler effects, Stark effects, and self-reversal of the lines are all reduced. The signal being emitted after a prescribed delay is used as the source, and is intermittent, stable, and has a narrow spectral width, all desirable features. However, experimental work by Strasheim and Butler (*9*) indicates that elaborate equipment is required and the signal is comparatively weak. One advantage stressed by Strasheim is that it is useful for simultaneous multielement analysis.

II. MODULATION

The importance of modulation to the accuracy of quantitative atomic absorption spectroscopy cannot be overemphasized. The problem is illustrated in Figure 2.6. The signal from the source has an intensity I_0. After passing through the atomizer, I_0 is reduced to I_1. However, in most atomizers (for example, a flame) the sample element emits at precisely the same wavelength as it absorbs. This is because the absorption line is usually a resonance

line, and, if the element emits atomic lines at all, it will
emit at this frequency. A decrease in the mechanical slit
width and thus the spectral slit width does not eliminate
this problem. It does cut down the unabsorbable background
which may fall on the detector and improves the ratio
$(I_0 - I_1)/I_0$. But the atoms which absorb at their resonance

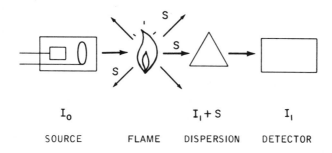

$$I_0 \qquad\qquad I_1 + S \qquad I_1$$

SOURCE   FLAME   DISPERSION   DETECTOR

FIGURE 2.6

Modulation of Equipment. $I_0 =$ Source Signal, $I_1 =$ Signal after
Absorption, and $S =$ Emission from the Atomizer. Modulation
Eliminates Signal S from Readout.

frequency also emit at precisely the same wavelength.
These two phenomena are not separated by cutting down
on the slit width, and the intensity of emitted radiation
will confound the absorption signal.

The effect is twofold. First, it reduces the apparent absorption signal. Instead of being equal to $(I_0 - I_1)$, it
becomes equal to $(I_0 - I_1) + S$, where S is the intensity
of emitted radiation from the flame at the absorption wavelength. This reduces sensitivity. Second, S is the same
signal as that used in flame photometry and is subject to
exactly the same errors. Therefore, operated under condi-

tions of no modulation, the process is subject to the errors of flame photometry and atomic-absorption spectroscopy. Further, there is a loss in sensitivity. These have led to erroneous interferences being reported from studies of inter-element effects in atomic-absorption spectroscopy.

It must be pointed out, however, that certain elements do not emit at their resonance frequencies and are not subject to this type of radiation interference. In general, these are elements that absorb strongly at wavelengths less than 3000 A. A classic example is zinc. However, since modulation is a minor modification to equipment, it seems unreasonable to limit instrumentation this way.

To overcome these problems, Walsh (1) ingeniously introduced the use of modulated instrumentation. The principle of the system is as follows. The output from the hollow cathode is modified from a dc to an ac signal. The detector is then tuned to the same frequency and synchronized. The result is that the detector becomes sensitive to the ac signal from the source and can perceive any absorption of the source radiation that takes place. However, the signal from the flame is dc. The detector is unable to register this signal and therefore only reads any change in signal from the hollow cathode source.

In practice, modulation is brought about by mechanical or electrical means. Using the electrical method, the power supply to the hollow cathode is either ac or is rectified to become intermittent dc. The light coming from the hollow cathode is intermittent in each case. The detector is tuned to this frequency and is synchronized to the light pulses. Any steady light from the flame atomizer affects I_0 and I_1 equally and the difference (absorption) is again $I_0 - I_1$.

In the mechanical method, the hollow cathode emits a steady beam of light. A metal disc, with two open opposite quadrants is placed off-center in the light path. The remaining quadrants chop off the light source. The disc is rotated at a controlled frequency and alternately allows the light to pass down the sample beam or blocks it. Further, the rotary chopper rapidly switches on and off the power

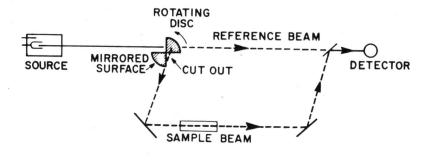

FIGURE 2.7

Schematic Diagram of a Mechanically Modulated System. On Rotating the Disc, the Light from the Source is Alternately Guided Down the Sample and Reference Beams.

supply to the detector. The latter is thereby tuned and synchronized to the intermittent light source (Figure 2.7). On rotating the disc, the light from the source is alternately guided down the sample and the reference beam.

III. ATOMIZERS

After light of the correct wavelength has been generated in the source, it is directed through the atomizer. Metal atoms absorb some of the light and provide the basis for atomic absorption. The function of the atomizer therefore is to take the sample and reduce the metal being determined from an ion, or a molecule to the neutral atomic state. This is the most difficult and the most inefficient step in the atomic-absorption process. The efficiency of all other steps is good, for example, the light source, monochromator, detector, and readout. Calculations show that the atomization step may be so poor as to reduce only one atom per million in the sample. This low efficiency is a severe limitation to sensitivity of detection. However, it also indicates the strides that are yet to be made in this field. The most common atomizers are described below.

A. Flame Atomizers

The only commercially available atomizers are burners. With minor modifications, these are the same as those used for flame photometry. Among their commercial advantages are the facts that they are cheap to manufacture and they are comparatively simple to operate. All burners accommodate only liquid samples. Two types are available, the total consumption burner and the burner based on Lundegardh's original design.

1. Total-Consumption Burner

The design of the total-consumption burner is shown in Figure 2.8. The flame is created by the oxidant (air or oxygen) and the fuel (hydrogen, acetylene, town gas, or cyanogen). Other exotic flames such as hydrogen-fluorine have been used, but have proved of academic interest only. The liquid sample is aspirated into the flame, and the metal is reduced to the ground state. This complicated step is considered in greater detail in Chapter 3, Section II. All the

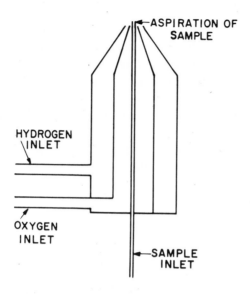

FIGURE 2.8

Design of a Total-Consumption Burner.

sample that is aspirated is injected into the flame, hence
the name *total-consumption burner*. The advantages of the
burner are as follows:

1. It is comparatively simple to manufacture.

2. A complete representative sample reaches the flame.

3. There is no explosive hazard from a mixture of unburned combustible gases.

Its chief disadvantages include the following:

1. Sample aspiration rate is a function of viscosity. This
varies between different solvents and with temperature
changes.

2. Very viscous samples cannot be aspirated at all.

3. The size of the drops of sample injected onto the base
of the flame vary over a wide range even under favorable
conditions.

4. Encrustation of the burner tip or blockage of the flow lines causes wide variations in the sample feed rate and hence in the absorption signal. This can easily escape the notice of the operator and result in serious errors unless corrected.

5. The burners are noisy, both physically and electronically.

As in flame photometry, however, with reasonable care, good precision can be achieved with total-consumption burners.

2. Lundegardh Burner

The second type of burner used extensively is based on Lundegardh's original flame-photometer burner and is shown in Figure 2.9. The same oxidants and fuels are used as in the total-consumption burner. These are premixed in the barrel of the burner. The sample is aspirated into the same barrel and an appreciable part is evaporated into the fuel-oxidant mixture. The whole mixture is then swept into the flame, and combustion takes place. Part of the sample (for example, large droplets) do not completely evaporate in the barrel. These run down the walls and finally drip out of the barrel as excess, unused sample. The entire aspirated sample does not reach the flame as it does in the total-consumption burner. This type of burner was favored by Walsh in much of his experimental work. Its advantages include the following:

1. The elongated burner introduces more atoms into the light path. This improves sensitivity.

2. Encrustation is reduced because large droplets are eliminated from the system.

3. It is quiet to operate.

Its disadvantages include the following:

1. With mixed solvents, the more volatile solvent is evaporated selectively. With some samples the metal components stay in the unevaporated portion and do not reach the burner. This produces serious errors in accuracy.

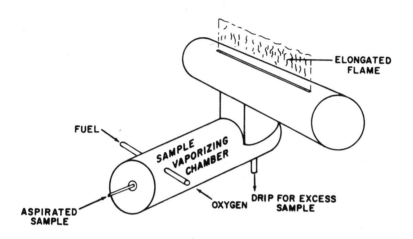

FIGURE 2.9

A Nebulizer Burner Based on the Lundegardh Burner (after the Perkin-Elmer 303).

2. The relatively large volumes of fuel-oxidant mixtures can be explosive. This eliminates the use of some mixtures, particularly oxy-acetylene.

3. Early models used base metal for the burner. Corrosive solvents caused these metals to dissolve and contaminate the flame. This problem was overcome by Clinton (*12*), who coated the burner tip with gold, which prevented further solution of the metal.

3. Forced-Feed Burner

An improvement of the total-consumption burner was made by Robinson and Harris (*13*). This burner is illustrated in Figure 2.10. The liquid sample was fed by mechanical displacement into the burner, thus assuring that the sample feed rate was constant irrespective of the viscosity of the sample. Different solvents can be fed at constant flow rates. This is important for continuous analysis of plant feed streams, where variations in temperature and composition and therefore viscosity can be expected. These changes would cause a change in sample feed rate and therefore an error in signal.

The liquid sample is subjected to the shearing action of high-pressure oxygen. These droplets are then sprayed into the flame. In this sense the instrument is a total-consumption burner. Studies with this burner showed that, when organic solvents were used, the absorption signal was enhanced over the signal obtained when aqueous solvents were used even at constant feed rates. However, the differences normally observed when different organic solvents were used was virtually eliminated. These results are considered further in the discussion on solvent effects (Chapter 3, Section V).

The general use of burners for atomization is probably the weakest link in the whole process of atomic-absorption spectroscopy. Their atomizing efficiency can be calculated to be very low (*14*). When new atomizers are developed, we can expect dramatic advances in sensitivity limits. Other means of atomization have been demonstrated successfully. In some cases very high sensitivity has been achieved. These are discussed below.

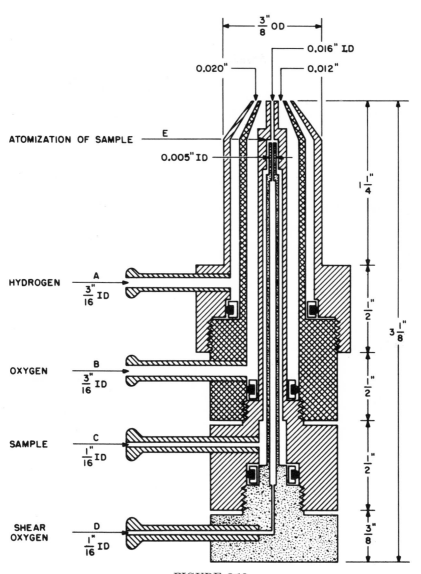

FIGURE 2.10

Schematic Diagram of a Mechanical-Feed Total-Consumption
Burner.

35

B. Hollow Cathode Atomizers

In common with much of the pioneering work in this field, this atomizer was developed by Gatehouse and Walsh (*15*) and is illustrated in Figure 2.11. This hollow cathode

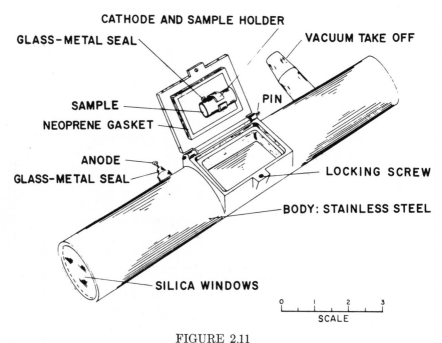

FIGURE 2.11

Sputtering-Type Atomizer.

atomizer was used for the direct analysis of metal samples. A small hole was drilled through the sample which was then mounted in the cathode and sample holder (Figure 2.11).

A potential difference of about 600 volts was then maintained between the anode and the cathode, in the same fashion as in a hollow cathode. Any air in the atomizer was swept out with a suitable inert gas such as helium, neon, or argon. The pressure was lowered to a pressure of 1 mm Hg, causing a discharge across the electrodes. As in the hollow cathode, sputtering of the cathode took place; thus neutral metal atoms were promoted into the atmosphere. The discharge was maintained for several minutes to clean-up the atomizer. It was then repurged with inert gas, and again the pressure was reduced to 1 mm Hg. The high voltage was then reapplied.

The sample holder is so arranged that the light path goes through the hole drilled through the sample. The atoms which were produced by sputtering then absorbed radiation from the hollow cathode light source, and the degree of absorption was measured.

To make this signal useful however it must be stable. Previous discussion of the hollow cathode showed that the rate of production of atoms from the hollow cathode is dependent, among other things, on the pressure of the filler gas. In a sealed unit the gas pressure is stable over long periods of time. However, in this instrument it would be very difficult to achieve and maintain a constant pressure. Further, since this device is intended for routine use, speed is the essence, making this step doubly difficult to perform.

As an alternative to the above, Jones and Walsh (2) proposed a second approach to overcome this problem. The proposal was as follows. After all the air was swept out, the pressure was continuously decreased. At a relatively high pressure, discharge between the electrodes began. However, at this high pressure the production of neutral atoms from the sample surface was inefficient. The short mean free path of the atoms was one reason for this.

When the pressure was reduced to low levels, the mean

free path of the charged filler gas atoms was satisfactory, but the total number of atoms striking the cathode was low. Again there was inefficiency in producing neutral atoms from the sample.

Between these extreme conditions is an optimum condition for atom production. If, therefore, the degree of absorption was measured continuously as the filler-gas pressure dropped, the signal should go through a maximum. Walsh has illustrated that this maximum can be used as a quantitative measure for the analysis of the sample. However, further studies have shown that the instrument can be operated successfully under conditions of constant pressure.

The principle advantage of this device is that metal samples can be analyzed directly, thus avoiding the tedious step of sample solution and separation. The atomizer should be handled with caution. It must be remembered that the whole sample is not atomized. Only the surface is exposed to sputtering, and consequently the analysis obtained is that of the surface only. With many alloys, etc., this does not represent a problem. However, two sources of error must always be considered. First, heterogenous samples such as rimming steels will give false analyses unless precautions are taken. Second, during the preparation of the sample, changes may take place at the sample surface. For example, when the sample is drilled it may get hot and lose some of the more volatile surface metals. This problem could arise with the determination of carbon in steel.

Although the total quantity of metal or carbon lost from the sample is very low, it all comes from the surface, and it is the surface which is being analyzed. Without proper precautions and interpretation serious errors can result. However, Gatehouse and Walsh successfully analyzed silver in copper, aluminum in zinc, and silicon in aluminum and steel (*15*).

Problems encountered with this procedure include poor reproducibility and preferential sputtering of some metals in certain alloys.

Goleb and Brody (*16*) used the same principle for analyzing liquid samples. An 0.1-ml sample was added to the sample cathode and evaporated evenly onto the sides. The sample cathode was mounted in the cathode holder and the analysis continued as before. High sensitivity was obtained in detecting magnesium, calcium, beryllium, silicon, and sodium. However, some interference from lithium and magnesium salts was observed with the sodium determination. No explanation has yet been proposed to explain this interference.

C. Electrical Discharges

An electrical discharge has been successfully used for the atomization of liquid samples (*17*). The advantage that this means of atomization has over flame atomizers is that it can easily reduce all metals, including aluminum, titanium, tungsten, and molybdenum. These metals form refractory oxides in flames and are only reduced to atoms under highly reducing conditions.

In principle, the liquid sample is sprayed into an electrical discharge similar to that used in emission spectrography. Atomization of the sample takes place. Absorption of radiation from the hollow cathode takes place in the normal fashion. An illustration of the experimental set-up is shown in Figure 2.12.

Although only scant data are available on the use of this atomizer, it seems that the efficiency of atomization should be better than that achieved in flames. For many metals, increased sensitivity could be expected—particularly for the

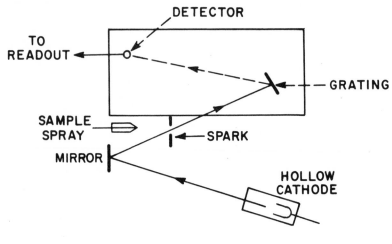

FIGURE 2.12

Atomization of Liquid Samples Using an Electrical Discharge.

metals that form refractory oxides in flames. Some experimental difficulties are involved in the method. Insulation of the liquid spray injected into the spark must be effective, particularly in view of the high voltages involved in spark discharges. It must be remembered that the spray itself will become a good electrical conductor under these conditions; hence the sample will be highly charged. A second problem is the strong electrical and magnetic radiation coming from the discharge. This is easily picked up by the wiring of the instrument, and a very noisy signal results. Unless special precautions are taken to eliminate pick-up of this radiation, it is impossible to perform quantitative analysis.

It must also be remembered that the emission signal from the discharge is high. As with the flame, this source of error can be eliminated by modulating the source and tuning the detector.

Through this procedure, a sensitivity of 1 ppm has been achieved for aluminum, at a wavelength of 3944 A (17).

D. Thermal Atomizers

Atomization of solid and liquid samples has been achieved by simply heating the sample in a controlled atmosphere. In each case the principle is the same. The sample is heated to a very high temperature, the metal atoms vaporize, and neutral atoms invade the surrounding atmosphere. If an inert atmosphere is used, the neutral atoms are stabilized and a high degree of absorption is obtained. The more successful methods of thermal atomization are described below.

1. Flash Heating Atomizer

Studies on this type of atomizers are still in the preliminary stages but appear encouraging. The equipment used is illustrated in Figure 2.13.

The sample is in the form of wire, ribbon, or powder. Powder samples are supported on quartz or graphite strips. The samples are contained in an enclosed tube and are flash heated by the intense radiation from a discharge lamp. In this fashion electrical energy is transferred as radiant energy to the sample. The advantages of this set-up are as follows:

1. An inert atmosphere stabilizes the neutral metal atoms formed.

2. The sample is isolated from the source of energy required for atomization, thus avoiding contamination of the sample, corrosion of the equipment, and memory effects from one sample to the next.

3. For routine purposes, the samples are easily interchangeable.

Much of the development work on this instrument has

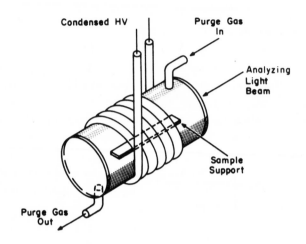

FIGURE 2.13

Experimental Flash Heating Atomizer.

been done by Nelson and Kuebler (*18*), who have reported intense absorption by copper, iron, europium, dysprosium, aluminum, boron, tungsten, gold, and lead. This seemingly useful atomizer still remains to be made available commercially.

2. The King Furnace

The King furnace has been modified by Vidale (*19*) for the measurement of the vapor pressure of sodium over glass, silicon over silicon carbide, etc. The equipment is illustrated in Figure 2.14. The sample is placed in a sealed quartz cell which is then inserted in a 20-in. quartz tube and put into a conventional heating furnace such as a Hevi-Duty Corp. split-core-tube furnace. The tube is capable of reaching a temperature of 1100°C. The furnace tube is

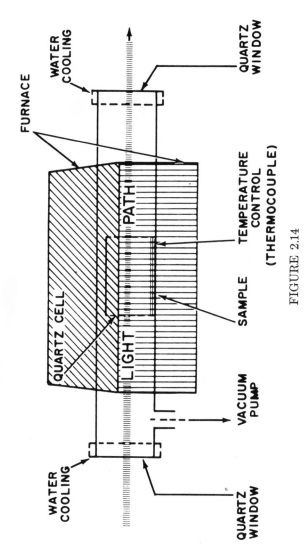

FIGURE 2.14

Modified King Furnace for Atomic Absorption.

fitted at each end with quartz windows and is placed concentric with the light beam.

On heating, neutral metal atoms from the sample pervade the atmosphere of the quartz cell and absorption of light takes place. Very high sensitivities have been claimed (10^{-10} g). Also, the modifications introduced by Vidale cut down the diffusion of the sample, enabling more reproducible results to be obtained. A precision of about 20 per cent has been obtained at the 10^{-10}-g level.

3. The L'vov Furnace

A further method is a high-temperature furnace developed by L'vov (20) for atomic-absorption spectroscopy. The furnace (Figure 2.15) is made of a hollow graphite tube placed concentric to the light beam. The graphite tube is preheated to a temperature of 2000 to 3000°K. It is wrapped on the inside with tantalum foil to prevent diffusion of the sample through the walls of the tube. In his original work, L'vov analyzed liquid samples, which were spotted onto the end of a carbon electrode and evaporated to dryness. The electrode was then introduced into the graphite furnace, and a dc arc was maintained for about 4 sec. The sample volatilized into the furnace and was reduced by the graphite. Intense absorption by neutral atoms took place. The degree of absorption rapidly decreased as the neutral atoms diffused from the end of the tube.

Continuous recording of the light signal was necessary to determine the maximum absorption. This occurred immediately after the arc was struck.

Samples weighing up to 100 μg were used, and absolute sensitivities between 10^{-8} and 5×10^{-11} g have been achieved. It is claimed that up to twenty samples can be

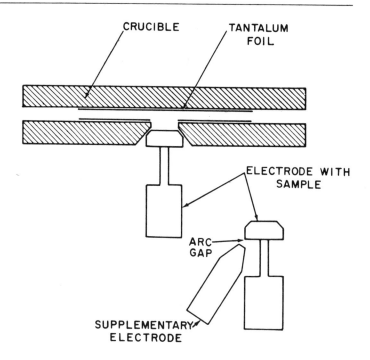

FIGURE 2.15

High-Temperature Furnace as Designed and Used by L'vov.

analyzed per hour. Limitations noted include the following:

1. There is difficulty in weighing or measuring the small samples required by the method.

2. Some elements have their resonance lines in the vacuum ultraviolet and cannot be determined with conventional equipment.

3. Some elements such as uranium, thorium, and zirconium have very low vapor pressures and weak absorption lines. Their atomization is very difficult and detection limits are poor.

In view of the high sensitivities achieved with these "nonflame" atomizers, it is surprising that they have not been commercially developed. The fact that there are no "flame" components to react with the neutral atoms should lead to high sensitivities and few interferences.

IV. MONOCHROMATORS

The monochromators used in the spectral regions of atomic absorption are prisms, gratings, and filters. In most applications to spectroscopy, the dispersion required for the problem at hand usually dictates the type of monochromator employed. However, this rule is not so important to atomic-absorption spectroscopy.

It will be remembered that the source emits very narrow lines and that the background is virtually zero. In general it is necessary only to separate the resonance line from other spectral lines in the immediate vicinity. These lines originate from the metals in the hollow cathode and the filler gas. Any emitted line (other than the absorption line), which falls on the detector will not be absorbed by the sample, and a severe loss in analytical sensitivity can result.

Workers in the field have defined the sensitivity limit as that concentration of metal which will diminish the signal by 1 per cent. If the intensity of the signal was I_0 before absorption and I_1 after absorption, we have at the sensitivity limit

$$\frac{I_0 - I_1}{I_0} = \frac{1}{100}$$

If, however, a second line of intensity I'_0 falls on the detector and is not absorbed by the sample, the same concentration which originally gave 1 per cent absorption will now give

$$\frac{(I_0 - I_1) + I'_0}{I_0 + I'_0}$$

How much analytical sensitivity is lost depends on the relative intensity of I_0 and I'_1. The greater I'_0, the more the loss in sensitivity.

Therefore, it can be seen that it is necessary to prevent unabsorbable lines from the hollow cathode in the vicinity of the absorption line from falling on the detector. However, because the background between the spectral lines is so low, further resolution is unnecessary.

For transition metals, high dispersion is usually necessary, but for many elements such as the alkali metals it is not. It is felt that filters could be used with a decrease in cost for routine instruments designed to determine only a few elements. However, this has not been done commercially, and only prism and grating instruments are available.

Prisms have been used extensively in the past. They are usually made of quartz. Their chief advantage is that the resolution they provide is adequate for many applications. Also, second- and third-order lines do not overlap and cause confusion. However, there are a number of analyses for which prism monochromators are inadequate.

Gratings are probably the most popular monochromator used commercially. They provide excellent resolution, satisfactory for all but the most demanding of applications. In the not-too-distant past their cost was prohibitive. However, replica gratings are now made and are of excellent quality. Their decreased cost makes possible their use in medium-priced equipment.

V. DETECTORS

Photographic film and photomultipliers have been used as detectors. Film, however, has not found wide acceptance.

As in emission spectrography, film suffers from the disadvantage that its sensitivity varies with wavelength and that its processing must be carefully controlled if reproducible results are to be obtained. When used for atomic absorption, there is an additional handicap. The absorption signal measured is the difference between I_0, the initial light intensity, and I_1, the light intensity after absorption. If a small quantity of light is absorbed, it is measured as the difference between two intense lines. On film this requires the measurement of two dark lines. A small percentage of error in the measurement of the intensity of either or both lines becomes a gross error in the measurement of the difference between them. The only successful use of film has been for qualitative analysis in which the purpose was to find if any absorption took place at high metal concentrations.

Photomultipliers have been used extensively and successfully. The most commonly used tubes have been the 1P28 and R106 in the ultraviolet and visible, and the 1P22 and selected R.C.A. 931A at longer wavelengths. The EMI-9529B has been used over the whole range. Commercial equipment which uses the 1P28 for wavelengths in the ultraviolet also uses the 1P22 for wavelength in the near infrared. The response curve for these two detectors is shown in Figure 2.16. It can readily be seen from these curves that, when a resonance line with a wavelength greater than 6000 A is being used, a 1P22 photomultiplier should be used, or a loss of signal will result. This loss of signal cannot be compensated for by extra amplification. This invariably increases the noise band of the response and the answers become unreliable.

The EMI9529B tube is a comparative newcomer to spectroscopy. In contrast to the 1P28 and 1P22, it is an end-on detector. Its response curve is shown in Figure 2.17.

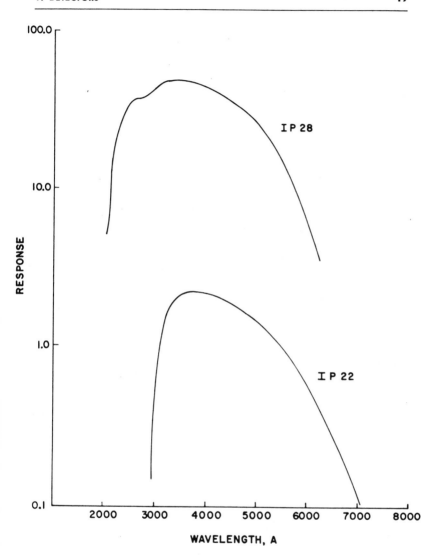

FIGURE 2.16

Response Curves for R.C.A. IP28 and IP22 Photoelectric
Detectors.

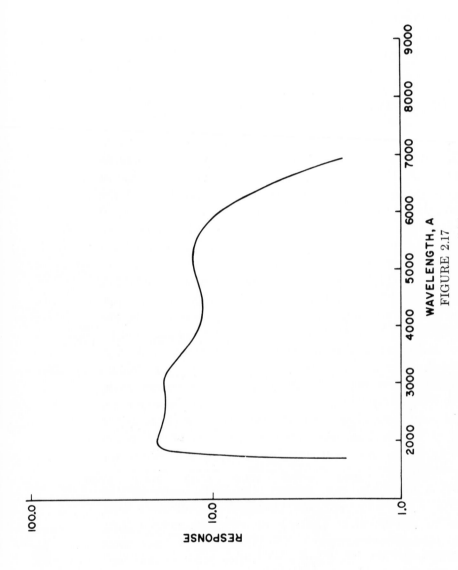

WAVELENGTH, A
FIGURE 2.17

Response Curve for EM19529B Photomultiplier Detector.

50

As the figure indicates the tube has a wide useful range and can be used for all elements hitherto analyzed by atomic-absorption spectroscopy.

VI. OPTICAL SYSTEMS

In common with all spectroscopic-absorption methods, either the single-beam or the double-beam system may be used. With single-beam optics, the intensity of the source line is measured as I_0. The sample is introduced into the system and the apparent intensity of the source line is measured as I_1. The absorbed light is determined as $I_0 - I_1$. Correction for any absorption by the flame and combustion products of the sample must be made.

To obtain high sensitivity, the signal I_0 must show a low noise level and a minimum drift. It must therefore be stable over short and long periods of time. To ensure this, the power supply to the hollow cathode must be of top quality. Not only must it produce power with a short- and long-term stability, it must also be able to correct for changes in the mains voltage that activates the power supply itself. In industrial areas these can be particularly severe when local companies close down for any reason, such as at the end of the working day. The requirements of the power supply can be met, but usually the equipment is not too expensive.

With a double-beam system, the light beam for the source is split into two paths. One path, the reference path, goes to the detector. The second path, the sample path, goes through the sample to the detector. The light beam can be split by using a mirrored surface such as that used for a mechanical modulation chopper. The chopper alternately passes and reflects the light beam, thus creating two separate and hopefully equal beams of light.

These two beams of light fall upon the detector alternately. The circuit is so arranged that, if they are equal, they balance each other and the detector generates no signal. However, if they are different, an imbalance is created in the circuit and the detector generates an alternating current. This current is amplified and measured. The advantage of this system is that the difference between the reference and the sample beams is measured—a direct measurement of the absorbed light. Any variation in the source is now of reduced importance and a less exacting demand is put on the power supply. This is a financial advantage to the manufacturer and used alike.

However, other than the financial advantage of the double-beam, there appears to be little difference in the sensitivity or precision of the two optical systems.

A. Two-Wavelength System

As an alternative to the double-beam system, two spectral lines of different wavelength have been used (*21, 22*). One of the lines chosen is not absorbed by the sample and can be considered the reference beam; the other is a resonance line and can be considered the sample beam. A schematic diagram of the equipment is shown in Figure 2.18.

The relative intensities of the two source lines are measured with no sample absorbing the resonance line. The sample is now put into the system and the relative intensities of the lines are measured again. By assuming that the unabsorbed line does not change in intensity, we can calculate the degree of the absorption of the resonance line. The principle advantage of the method is that both sample and reference beams traverse the sample. Any apparent absorption of light by materials other than the sample, for example, by solid particles in the flame will affect both beams equally and a correction will automatically be made. One possible source of error is a change in the relative intensities of the two lines emitted from the source. For example, if the voltage to the hollow cathode varies, it is possible that the relative intensities of the different emitted

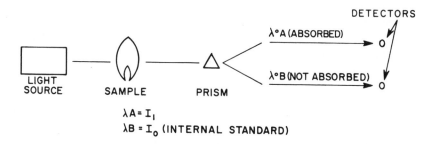

FIGURE 2.18

A Schematic Diagram of a Two-Wavelength Optical System.

lines might vary. To answer this question, the voltage to an iron hollow cathode was varied by 50 per cent (*22*). It was found that the relative intensity of the unabsorbed Fe (3787 A) to the absorbed (3719 A) varied less than 2 per cent. This relationship held true for many pairs of lines, but a few lines did show some change. It was concluded that, with proper care in selecting the reference or non-absorbed line, the method could be used satisfactorily.

The principle has never been exploited commercially. However, it is felt that where high sensitivity and precision are required the method holds promise.

B. Multipass System

As a method of increasing sensitivity, Russell et al. (*23*) demonstrated that the light beam could be reflected through the flame of an atomizer several times. Each time the light beam traversed the flame, more light was absorbed by the neutral atoms present. The process worked successfully for twelve reflections. This gave about ten times as much absorption as a single pass. The method has been successfully incorporated into the Jarral Ash equipment. It is limited ultimately by the loss of light on reflection. After numerous reflections, I_0 becomes too low to be adequate. Perhaps the new more intense sources will help encourage further use of this system.

VII. POWER SUPPLY TO THE HOLLOW CATHODE

As indicated earlier, the demands placed on the power supply depend on the equipment used. For an electrically modulated instrument the power should be ac; for equipment modulated mechanically, dc. For single-beam instrumentation, high stability is required, and noise and drift should be at a minimum. However, for a double-beam operation, the stability requirements are not so exacting. Although noise is always undesirable, much of the effect of short-term and long-term drift is corrected for by the double-beam system.

Ideally, the power supply should be capable of delivering up to 1000 volts and up to 50 ma. High power input is useful in producing intense light sources. This in turn decreases the required amplification of the signal and allows the detector to be operated at low voltage. The noise level of the readout signal is thereby reduced with an accompanying gain in precision.

Unfortunately, most commercial instruments do not use a power supply with such a high output. The reasons are two. First, most analytical requirements are met even when a lower output is used. Second, a high output can easily be misused if set into the hands of inexperienced operators. Many hollow cathodes have a very short life when operated at high voltage. The metal of the hollow cathode sputters too fast and "boils" into the main body of the source. Only high-boiling stable metals such as iron or titanium could be used safely at high voltages. Therefore, the low-voltage power supplies used in commercial equipment act as a safety factor for the hollow cathode.

REFERENCES

1. A. Walsh, *Spectrochim. Acta,* **7**, 108 (1955).
2. W. G. Jones and A. Walsh, *Spectrochim. Acta,* **16**, 249 (1960).
3. H. M. Crosswhite, G. H. Dieke, and C. S. Legangeur, *J. Opt. Soc. Am.,* **45**, 270 (1955).
4. *Perkin-Elmer Corp. Newsletter,* Vol. 3.11, December 1964.
5. A. Walsh, L.S.U. Intern. Symp. Modern Methods of Analytical Chemistry, January 1962.
6. H. Massman, *Z. Instrumentenk,* **71**, 225 (1963).
7. L. R. P. Butler and A. Strasheim, Pittsburgh Conference of Analytical Chemistry and Applied Spectroscopy, March 1964.
8. S. R. Koirtyohann and C. Feldman, *Develop. Appl. Spectry.,* **3**, 180 (1963).
9. A. Strasheim and L. R. P. Butler, *Appl. Spectry.,* **16**, 109 (1962).
10. D. W. Cooke, L.S.U. Intern. Symp. Modern Methods of Analytical Chemistry, 1961.
11. A. Strasheim, *Nature,* **196**, 1194 (1962).
12. O. E. Clinton, *Spectrochim. Acta,* **16**, 985 (1960).
13. J. W. Robinson and R. J. Harris, *Anal. Chim. Acta,* **26**, 439 (1962).
14. J. W. Robinson, *Develop. Appl. Spectry.,* **4**, 455 (1965).

15. B. M. Gatehouse and A. Walsh, *Spectrochim. Acta,* **16**, 602 (1960).

16. J. A. Goleb and J. K. Brody, *Anal. Chim. Acta,* **28**, 457 (1963).

17. J. W. Robinson, *Anal. Chim. Acta,* **27**, 465 (1962).

18. L. S. Nelson and N. A. Kuebler, *Spectrochim. Acta,* **19**, 781 (1963).

19. G. L. Vidale, Space Science Lab., Aerospace Operation, General Electric T.I.S. Rep. R60SD330 (1960).

20. D. V. L'vov, *Spectrochim. Acta,* **17**, 761 (1961).

21. A. C. Menzies, *Anal. Chem.,* **32**, 898 (1960).

22. J. W. Robinson, *Anal. Chem.,* **33**, 1226 (1961).

23. B. J. Russell, J. P. Shelton, and A. Walsh, *Spectrochim. Acta,* **8**, 317 (1957).

CHAPTER THREE

Analytical Parameters

The ultimate object of analytical chemistry is to obtain accurate and reproducible results. To do this, it is imperative that we understand clearly what is being measured and what variables will affect the measurement.

We have already seen that the extent of absorption is given by the expression

$$\int K\nu \, d\nu = \frac{\pi e^2}{mc} Nf \qquad (3.1)$$

As explained earlier, for a given resonance wavelength the only variable over which we have any control is N, the number of absorbing atoms. The most important variable is therefore N, the number of absorbing atoms in the light path.

The physics involved in the absorption of light of the correct wavelength by atoms is well-defined and amply understood for its application to analytical chemistry. If this were the sum total of the problem, we would indeed be blessed with a beautifully simple procedure.

Unfortunately, one other step is involved, and that is the production of neutral atoms from the sample. The efficiency of this step is very low and is affected by many variables.

I. ABSORPTION WAVELENGTH

When light is absorbed, an electron of the absorbing atom moves from one orbital to an orbital of higher energy. In Equation (3.1) N refers to the number of atoms with the absorbing electron in the lower-energy state of a pair of energy states. In theory the electronic transition can be between any pair of orbitals for which the transition is not forbidden. It is possible for an electron to absorb energy and move from one excited level to a more highly excited level. In practice however, the lower-energy state is always a ground state. The relative population of the various excited states is so low compared to the population of the ground state that absorption wavelengths involving transitions from one excited state to a higher excited state have not yet been shown to be useful. A simple calculation will illustrate the point.

For thermal excitation, the number N_2 of excited atoms

in equilibrium with atoms in the ground state is given by the expression

$$N_2 = N_1 \frac{g_1}{g_2} e^{-E/kT} \qquad (3.2)$$

where N_2 = number of atoms in excited state
     N_1 = number of atoms in ground state
     E = energy of excitation
     T = temperature
     g_1/g_2 = a priori probability of the ratio of the atoms in the ground state and the excited state

The quantity of energy involved is a function of the frequency involved, and is described by the expression

$$E = h\nu \qquad (3.3)$$

At short wavelengths, the energy E is high and at long wavelengths it is low. Typical relative populations of excited and ground state atoms in a system are given in Table 3.1. From this table we can see that, even under the

TABLE 3.1
THE EFFECT OF EXCITATION WAVELENGTH
ON THE POPULATION OF EXCITED ATOMS

Metal	Wavelength, A	N_2/N_1, ratio excited to unexcited atoms (temp = 3000°K)
Na	5890	5.9×10^{-4}
Zn	2139	5.6×10^{-10}

favorable conditions of high temperature and low excitation-energy requirements, the number of atoms in the excited state is small. This means that, even with sodium, which is easily excited, the number of excited atoms is small; therefore the number that can absorb energy and undergo transition starting from an excited energy level is also small. When we calculate the population of excited atoms which require high energy excitation (such as zinc) we can see that the population is extremely small. In contrast, the number of ground-state atoms of either sodium or zinc constitutes almost the whole neutral atom population. We can therefore conclude the following:

1. The degree of absorption is a function of the number of atoms which can absorb light of the wavelength used.

2. In a given population of atoms, the number of excited atoms is small compared to the number of unexcited atoms, even at high temperatures.

3. Apart from exceptional conditions, the great majority of neutral atoms are in the ground state.

4. The wavelength of light used should therefore be such as to excite ground-state atoms to an excited state.

When setting up an analytical procedure we must first choose a wavelength to satisfy these requirements. Expressed simply, we must choose a spectral line originating in the ground state so that N approaches the total population of neutral atoms present.

Fortunately, this does not restrict us to only one wavelength. For each element we find that several transitions are possible, each starting at the ground-state level. This is illustrated in Figure 3.1, where in addition to the ground state, three excited energy levels are shown. Each energy level has two spin states, and in each case a doublet is produced. The wavelength of light which must be absorbed to cause these transitions is given. For each transition the oscillator strength f varies significantly.

If we now re-examine Equation (3.1), we find that, for a

given population N, the degree of absorption is controlled by f, the oscillator strength. This in turn controls the sensitivity of the analytical procedure.

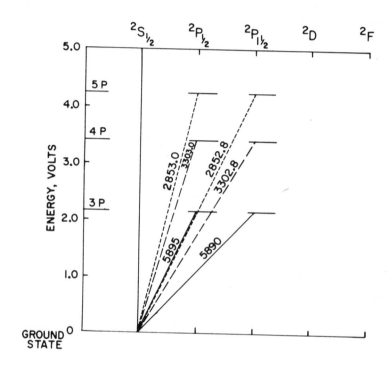

FIGURE 3.1

Partial Grotian Diagram for Sodium.

By choosing an absorption line in which f is high, we see that the analytical sensitivity will be high. If we choose a line in which f is low, the sensitivity will be low. Therefore, for any particular metal we may change our analytical range from the parts-per-million level to the fractional per cent level merely by changing the wavelength of absorption. In summary, the choice of wavelength for absorption is governed by two considerations: (1) the energy transition must be from a ground state to an excited state, and (2) the particular energy transition chosen will be based on the analytical range desired. This defines the wavelength of light to be used for absorption.

II. ATOMIZERS

The production of atoms from a given sample is the function of the atomizer. In general atomizers are quite inefficient. For example, with a flame atomizer, the detection limit for copper $(\lambda = 3247 \text{ A})$ is 0.1 ppm.

A solution of copper containing 63 g of copper per liter contains a total of 6×10^{23} ions of copper. For a solution containing 0.1 ppm of copper, the concentration is

$$0.1 \text{ ppm} = 0.0001 \text{ g/liter} \doteqdot 10^{18} \text{ ions/liter}$$
$$\doteqdot 10^{15} \text{ ions/ml}$$

If the feed rate is 1 ml/min and each ion is in the light path 1/0.01 min, the number of ions exposed at any particular instant is about 10^{13}. However, if we take Equation (3.1) and define the absorption as 1 per cent (conventional definition of the detection limit), then

$$\int K_\nu d_\nu = 0.01 = \frac{\pi e^2}{mc} Nf$$

and

$$N \doteqdot 10^8$$

where $N =$ the number of absorbing atoms.

At first glance it appears that, from the original sample containing 0.1 ppm of copper, only one copper atom in 10^5

is reduced to the atomic state. However, we cannot ignore the mismatch between the source wavelength and line width and between the absorption wavelength and its spectral line width. Even so, it would seem safe to say that sensitivities a thousand times better than those attained to date should be available to us with better atomization.

Various atomizers have already been described. Nevertheless, it seems pertinent to examine the most popular atomizer, the flame, from the point of view of its atomization efficiency and factors which affect this efficiency.

A. Flame Atomizers

Two types of burners have been used extensively in atomic absorption. Their construction has been described in Chapter 2, Sections III.A.1 and 2. Their use as atomizers is deceptively easy, and unless care is taken erroneous results will be obtained. A number of factors affect the absorption signal arising from a given solution.

The factors affecting total-consumption burners will now be discussed. These factors affect Lundegardh burners to a lesser or greater degree.

1. Flame Atom Population Profile

The normal flame from the total-consumption burner is about 3 in. high. If the sample is aspirated into the flame and the light beam is passed through its different parts, it is found that the absorption signal is not constant.

The relationship between absorption signal and flame height is called the flame profile. A typical profile is shown in Figure 3.2 from which it can be seen that, as the height of the light path above the base of the flame is increased, the degree of absorption first increases, then goes through a maximum, and finally diminishes to zero at the top of the flame. This change is caused by a change in the number of neutral atoms in different parts of the flame. The profile indicates the relative population of neutral atoms in the flame. It will also be noted that the position in the flame

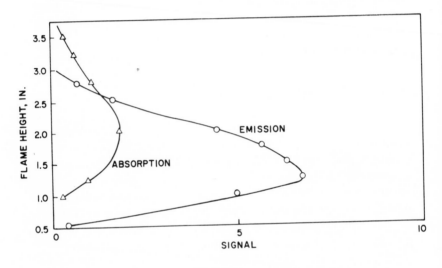

FIGURE 3.2

Flame Emission and Absorption Profile for Ni 3414-A Resonance Line. Sample: $NiCl_2$ (10 ppm) in Ethanol Oxyhydrogen Flame under Oxidizing Conditions.

at which maximum absorption takes place does not coincide with the zone of maximum spectral emission. Presumably this is because the lifetime of an excited atom, which is responsible for emission, is short (10^{-6} to 10^{-8} sec). Emission is therefore observed close to the position at which excited atoms are formed. On the other hand, absorption takes place by neutral atoms, which are stable compared to excited atoms. Neutral atoms are generated in all parts of the flame, and it can be seen that those formed in the lower parts will accumulate as they move into the upper regions.

When a sample is injected into a flame, it usually reaches the flame as a droplet. The process of forming atoms from liquid droplets is very complicated. It takes place in numerous steps and the efficiency of each step affects the final efficiency of producing neutral atoms from the sample solution.

A summary of the most important factors and their inter-

TABLE 3.2
FACTORS AFFECTING FLAME PROFILES

Physical form of sample in flame	Reaction	Factors controlling reaction	Part of flame
Oxide	No reaction or reduction	Stability of metal oxide, flame composition	Outer mantle
Atoms	Accumulation or oxidation	Flame composition, stability of atoms	Reaction zone
Solid particles	Disintegration	Stability of compound, anions, flame temperature, ultraviolet light emitted from the flame	Inner cone
Droplets	Evaporation	Droplet size, solvent, flame temperature, feed rate, combustibility	Base

relationships is given in Table 3.2. It will be appreciated of course, that many of the larger droplets never evaporate and pass through the flame virtually unaffected. Also in many instances the residue left after evaporation of the smaller droplet also passes through the remainder of the flame unchanged. In both cases the metal atoms in these fragments will not contribute to the absorption signal and are wasted in the process.

There are two major parts of the flame absorption profile: the region at the base of the flame, where the absorption signal increases, and the part at the top, where the signal decreases. The first part is a reflection of the rate of formation of atoms, the second part is controlled by the rate of loss of atoms.

2. Droplet Size

If the burner aspirates the sample and forms large solvent droplets, these will evaporate relatively slowly and may pass completely through the flame and emerge as small droplets. In general, any metals in these drops will not contribute to the absorption signal. If, on the other hand, the drop size is small, evaporation takes place rapidly and reduction of the metal ions to neutral atoms is more easily effected. Most commercial burners produce large-, small-, and intermediate-sized droplets and operate at an acceptable but not optimum efficiency.

When the solvent portion of a droplet is evaporated, a residue of metal ions, anions, and sundry other material remains. If the sample was originally inorganic the metal would probably now be in the form of a salt. If this salt is stable it is difficult to decompose it in the flame and the production of neutral atoms is inefficient. On the other hand, if the salt is easily decomposed by the flame, the production of neutral metal atoms is high and the absorption signal is high. The different absorption signals observed between different salts of a given metal at constant concentration is the heart of chemical interference and will be discussed later. The production of neutral atoms from the residue is therefore dependent on the stability of the compounds formed and the size of the droplets entering the flame.

3. Sample Feed Rate

Droplet evaporation and residue disintegration require energy. The energy must be provided by the flame. Under controlled conditions, the flame produces energy at a steady rate. If the sample feed rate is too high, too much of the energy of the flame is used in evaporating the sample and the remaining reduction steps are inefficient. In this case the flame has been swamped with sample. If the feed rate is too low, the production of neutral atoms is reduced and the signal is again low. Between these extremes there is an optimum feed rate, which varies with burner design, and even varies between different burners of the same design. In general it is observed that, if the flame is not swamped, an increase in sample feed rate results in an increase in absorption signal. For reproducible results, the feed rate must be kept constant. Unsuspected changes can be caused by blockage or encrustation of the burner tip. These sources of error should be checked at all times.

4. Flame Energy

As described above, the energy of the flame is used to produce neutral atoms from the solution; it exists in two

forms—thermal and spectral. The effect of the thermal
energy or temperature is well-documented. Certain elements
can be detected in high-temperature flames (such as oxyhydrogen) but not in low-temperature flames (such as air-
town gas). Also, chemical interferences are reduced in high-
temperature flames. This is because more thermal energy is
available in high-temperature flames to break down the
chemical compounds in the droplet residues. This is
equivalent to a drop in chemical interferences.

The effect of spectral energy is more subtle. It
seems reasonable to suppose that both droplets and residue will absorb spectral energy emitted by the flame
and that this would speed their disintegration. It has been
shown that iron emission lines are found at wavelengths
down to 2100 A in reducing oxycyanogen flames, but not in
oxidizing oxycyanogen flames at the same temperature (1).
The reducing flame emits intense ultraviolet radiation, and
this may be responsible for the iron reduction and excitation. However, no other verification of this proposal has
been made. It should be pointed out that the high atomization efficiency enjoyed by the reducing oxyacetylene flame
may be attributed at least in part to the intense incandescent nature of the flame, that is, to its high radiant
energy.

5. Oxide Formation

After metals in the sample have been reduced to neutral
atoms, they will stay in this state for varying periods of
time. This time period is ended if and when the atom becomes oxidized. Of course, a flame is created by the oxidation of a fuel, so it is not surprising that the metal atoms
also become oxidized even in "reducing" flames. If must be

remembered that a reducing flame is not a reduction process, but a flame in which there is more fuel than oxygen. It is still an oxidation process. Reduction may take place if the excess fuel reduces any metal oxide formed in the flame back to the free metal.

The ease with which the metal is oxidized is part of the chemistry of the particular metal. If the oxide is stable it will oxidize easily and vice versa. This step then is controlled by equilibrium:

$$\text{metal} + \text{oxygen} \xrightarrow{K_{eq}} \text{metal oxide} \qquad (3.4)$$

It can be calculated that K_{eq} at 3000°C for silver is about $10^{-2.7}$ and for magnesium is $10^{1.9}$. Their respective flame

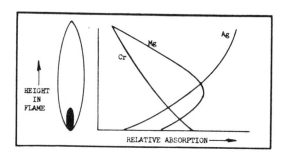

FIGURE 3.3

Flame Absorption Profile for Silver and Magnesium:

Metal	Flame height for maximum absorption	Predicted stability of oxide
Cr	Low	High
Mg	Medium	Medium
Ag	High	Low

profiles are shown in Figure 3.3, which illustrates that the flame profiles are markedly different. Magnesium gives a sharp maximum. It is very important to locate this maximum if good analytical precision is to be obtained on a day-to-day basis. It must be remembered, of course, that the total height of the flame may vary somewhat each day. This in turn would cause a change in the absolute height of the absorption maximum from the base of the flame. It is therefore necessary to relocate the absorption maximum each day and to position it in the light path.

The maximum for silver is never reached. It appears that silver oxide does not easily form and that accumulation of neutral atoms takes place in the higher parts of the flame. Day-to-day variations of the flame are not so critical in this case.

6. Variation in the Ratio of Fuel to Oxygen in the Flame

Like all chemical reactions, the oxidation of the metal is influenced by the affinity of the metal for oxygen and by the availability of the oxygen. The availability of oxygen in the flame is directly controlled by the flame composition. If it is an oxidizing flame, there is an excess of hot oxygen present and oxidation of the metal atom is promoted. However, if it is a reducing flame, there is an excess of fuel and presumably only reduced amounts of hot oxygen. This of course would prolong the life of the neutral atoms. That oxygen is still present in reducing flames is evidenced by the fact that we are still speaking of a portion of a flame which itself is created by the oxygen-fuel reaction. It must be remembered also that with conventional fuels there is an abundance of hot water molecules and of OH, O_2H, and other reactive chemical entities. These too are capable of oxidizing the neutral atoms in reducing flames.

7. Nitrous Oxide-Acetylene Flames

Recently Amos (2) has demonstrated the use of a nitrous oxide-acetylene flame. This flame requires the use of laminar-flow burners to assure maximum atomization.

The use of nitrous oxide instead of oxygen as the oxidant reduces the probability of the metal atom becoming rapidly oxidized in the flame. Preliminary results (2) using this flame have been very encouraging, particularly with regard to metals which form refractory oxides. Table 3.3 indicates

TABLE 3.3
SENSITIVITIES USING NITROUS
OXIDE-ACETYLENE FLAMES

Element	Sensitivity, ppm (1% absorption)
Be	0.02
Ge	5.5
B	90
Si	10
V	2
W	17
Nb	27
Zr	9
Hf	12
Ta	15
Ti	2
Al	1

the sensitivities achieved by Amos in his preliminary studies. No doubt these will be improved upon as further development is carried out.

8. Conclusion

Most atoms of the metallic elements undergo ultimate oxidation in the flame, particularly when air or oxygen is used as the oxidant. If we remember the oxidizing nature of flames, it would seem that the high analytical sensitivities achieved are better than we might justifiably expect, particularly in view of the high sensitivities achieved with nitrous oxide-acetylene flames. It would seem that flames have been studied and exploited almost to the limit of their usefulness. Significant advances in lowering sensitivity limits might reasonably be expected to be obtained using a different type of atomizer.

III. CATIONS

The effect of different cations on the absorption signal of the sample element is very small. In general, other metals present have no effect whatsoever, even at high concentrations. No cases have been noted where two metals absorb at the same wavelength and interfere with each other. On the contrary, even isotopes of the same element absorb at different wavelengths. By using a hollow cathode of one particular isotope of an element, we can determine the concentration of that isotope in the presence of other isotopes of the same element. This has been done with lithium 6 and 7 (3).

A well-documented case of interference however is the

mutual interference of magnesium and aluminum (4). When these two metals are present in the same solution and are aspirated into a flame, instead of being reduced to atoms, they form an intermetallic compound. This formation takes place in the residue left after evaporating the solvent, and not by interaction of the atom in the flame. This point was proved by aspirating each metal separately from two burners into a common flame. Under these experimental conditions, no interference was observed.

The interference using a single burner was noted in 1960. Recently, a similar interference has been found with calcium analysis. In this case beryllium, aluminum, and magnesium all caused cationic interference (5). However, the few interferences recorded show that this is very unusual and not to be considered a common source of interference in atomic absorption. It is probably chemical in nature. The neutral atoms may be removed by the formation of an intermetallic compound in the flame, or by the formation of salts such as aluminates.

It must be pointed out, however, that there have been a number of reports made of cationic interferences. In several of these instances the observations were made with unmodulated equipment. A lack of modulation permits radiation interference from emission bands and lines from other cations. This causes a change in the signal recorded by the detector and therefore an error in the apparent absorption signal.

To illustrate this point, let us suppose that the unabsorbed signal from the source is I_0 and that after absorption the signal is I_1. The degree of absorption is $I_0 - I_1$. If, however, light of intensity S is emitted from the burner at the same wavelength, the detector will not read out I_1 but $I_1 + S$. The apparent absorption will be $I_0 - (I_1 + S)$. This error can only be satisfactorily eliminated with modulated equipment. The use of calibration curves made from standard solutions similar to the sample diminishes the error, but the error can only be eliminated when the sample and the standards are identical. This happy state can sometimes be achieved in highly routine type of samples of virtually constant composition. But in all other cases, this source of error should be remembered and, if possible, corrections made. The error is best eliminated by modulating the equipment and avoiding the problem.

IV. ANIONS

To produce neutral atoms, the metal-anion bond must first be broken. The strength of this bond determines how easily this step can be taken. A strong metal-anion bond is difficult to break, and for a given atomizer system the production of atoms will be less efficient. On the other hand, a weak metal-anion bond is more easily broken, and the production of atoms in the same atomizer system would be greater. It is easy to see that, for a given concentration of metal ions in solution, the absorption signal may vary depending on the predominant anions present.

If the metal is combined with an organic addend, the situation is somewhat modified. The organic addend burns in the flame and the metal is liberated more easily. This results in a greater absorption signal with corresponding increase in sensitivity.

A summary of the effects of the chemical form of the metal in the sample is shown in Table 3.4.

The interference caused by the presence of different anions is called chemical interference. The same type of interference is encountered in flame photometry and emission spectrography. For many metals, the effect can be

TABLE 3.4
The Effect of Changing the Metal Compound Form
on the Absorption Signal

Compound	Solvent	Chromium absorption signal, $I_0 - I_1$ ($I_0 = 100$)
Chromic nitrate	Ethanol	20.5
Sodium chromate	Ethanol	18.2
Chromium naphthenate	Ethanol	26.3

TABLE 3.5
Chemical Interference and Its Elimination

Conditions	
Sample	Lead nitrate solution, 1.0 ppm
Wavelength	2170 A
Flame	Oxy-hydrogen 30 liters/min:50 liters/min
Burner	Beckman total-consumption
Aqueous	Solution

Absorption, %

Interfering anion (100 ppm)	Lead nitrate solution, plus interfering anion	Lead solution plus anion plus EDTA (1%)
None	23.0	23.0
PO^{3-}	19.9	22.8
Cl^-	22.3	22.3
CO_3^{2-}	12.8	23.0
I^-	13.7	23.5
SO_4^{2-}	22.0	23.0
F^-	21.3	22.9

reduced or eliminated by using a complexing agent. For example, by adding EDTA to various lead salts, chemical interference can be eliminated. This is illustrated in Table 3.5. Notice that serious anionic interference took place with lead before EDTA was added to the solution.

V. THE EFFECT OF DIFFERENT SOLVENTS

The solvent has several direct and indirect effects on the absorption signal. These are caused by (1) the spectral emission from the combustion products of the solvent; (2) spectral absorption by the solvent or its products in the flame; (3) the effect of the solvent on the efficiency of producing neutral atoms from the sample; (4) the change in sample feed rate with solvents having different viscosities; (5) the effect of surface tension on drop size.

A. Spectral Emission from the Solvent-Combustion Products

If we examine the emission signal from simple flames, we can observe several identifiable emission bands, and if we aspirate aqueous or organic solvents into the flame, we find that more emission bands appear. The emission from such flame systems has been studied extensively by Gaydon (*6*). There is no need to explore the origin of the variables of these emission spectra in the present work. However, it is important to know that such emission does take place.

The problem and the solution to the problem are the same as for cationic emission interferences. If the equipment is not modulated, the apparent absorption signal will not be $I_0 - I_1$ but $I_0 - (I_1 + S)$, where S is the emission from the flame. The intensity of S varies with the conditions used. Important factors to consider include the type of fuel and oxidant used for the flame, the ratio of the fuel and oxidant, the actual solvent used, the part of the flame through which the light beam travels, and the spectral range used for analysis. Figure 3.4 shows typical emission spectra for various solvents. It can be seen that at some wavelengths this emission is intense and can cause serious error. However, at other wavelengths there is no emission and therefore no error.

As in the case of cationic emission, the problem can be eliminated by modulating the equipment. The detector sees the alternating signal from the source, but not the steady emission signal from the flame. The detector registers $I_0 - I_1$ as the absorption signal, and the source of error is removed.

B. Absorption of Spectral Energy by the Flame and Solvents

The absorption spectrum of acetylacetone, aspirated into an oxyhydrogen flame is shown in Figure 3.5. This spectrum was obtained by using a hydrogen lamp as the light source, passing the beam through a flame, and recording $I_0 - I_1$ versus wavelength in the usual fashion (5).

It was also found that oxyhydrogen flames absorb over an extensive spectral range. The absorption was particularly strong between the wavelengths 2800 to 2860 and 3060 to 3200 A. However, it was found that the absorption bands were not continuous. Table 3.6 shows a list of the wavelengths of spectral lines that were absorbed and a second list of lines in the same spectral region, that were not absorbed.

Although the absorption is not intense, it is still not negligible. For accurate analysis, corrections must be made.

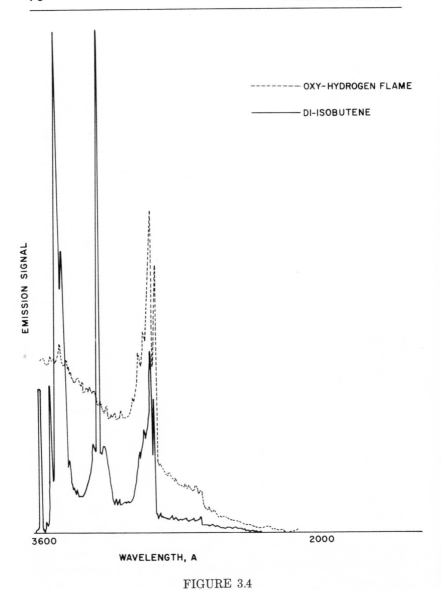

FIGURE 3.4

The Emission Spectra of Various Solvents in an Oxyhydrogen
Flame.

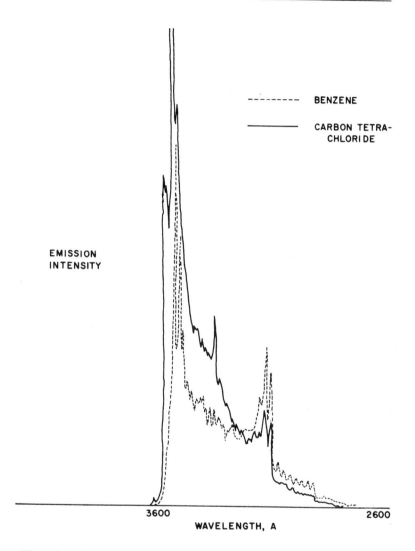

The absorbing component has not been positively identified but is probably OH moieties. Aspiration of water into an oxyhydrogen flame usually increases the absorption, but if the flame is swamped, breakdown of the water into OH radicals is not efficient and the flame absorption is decreased. Unfortunately, under these conditions the liberation of neutral atoms from the sample is also inefficient and low analytical sensitivity results. Swamping the flame

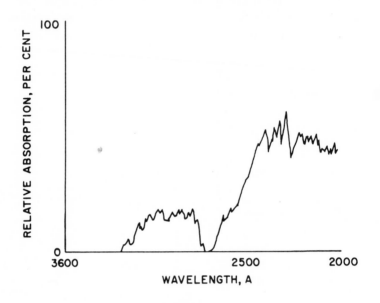

FIGURE 3.5

The Absorption Spectrum of an Oxyhydrogen Flame Burning Acetylacetone. The Shape and Height of the Curve is very Susceptible to Flame Conditions and to the Part of the Flame Examined.

to eliminate flame absorption is like curing the disease, but killing the patient.

It has also been observed that, when different organic solvents are aspirated into the flame, the total absorption by the flame plus solvent is different—usually it is increased. Also, with the lead 2170-A line, it has been observed that the hydrogen gas causes strong absorption even at room temperature. The same line is also absorbed by an oxy-hydrogen flame. It is conceivable that the absorption is caused by unreacted hydrogen.

In summary it must be concluded that the flame itself may absorb at the wavelength of interest. The extent of flame absorption may be changed by the solvent of the

TABLE 3.6

THE ABSORPTION OF VARIOUS EMISSION LINES
BY OXYHYDROGEN FLAMES

Hollow cathode lines absorbed, wavelength, A	Hollow cathode lines not absorbed, wavelength, A
2802	2818
2824	2823
2830	2840
2833	2851
3065	3094
3103	3118
3175	3141

sample. The best way to correct for this source of error is first to measure the absorption of the flame plus the solvent used in the sample. Next the total absorption of the flame, solvent, and sample is measured. The difference between the readings is the net absorption of the sample element. This is the figure which should be used for the final calculation of the analysis of the sample. The problem of absorption by the products of combustion can be serious when flame adapters are used. These are discussed in Chapter 3, Section VII.

C. Effect of Solvents on the Efficiency of Producing Neutral Atoms

It has been observed on numerous occasions that enhancement of signal takes place if an organic solvent is used instead of an aqueous solvent. For flame atomizers, there is an enhancement of both absorption and emission signal. Typical results for 10-ppm nickel solutions are shown in Table 3.7.

TABLE 3.7

EFFECT OF SOLVENT ON NICKEL ABSORPTION
AND EMISSION SIGNALS (7)

Solvent[a]	Emission	Absorption
Water	4	4
Acetone	18	144
n-Pentane	19	66
Xylene	17	30

[a] *Experimental conditions:* nickel concentration = 10 ppm, absorption wavelength = 3414 A, total-consumption burner.

The enhancement effect of organic solvents was first observed in emission flame photometry. The first explanation suggested was that the organic solvent increased the flame temperature, and that this in turn increased the emission intensity. However, if this proposal was true, for a given population of atoms, the number of excited atoms would increase, but the number of unexcited atoms would simultaneously decrease. This is expressed numerically in Table 3.8.

The number of atoms given in Table 3.8 are not to be taken literally, but are proposed only for the purpose of demonstration. However, it can be seen that, if thermal excitation was the only effect of the organic solvent, the absorption effect should actually decrease slightly. However, the data of Table 3.7 showed that both absorption and emission signals increased. This can be satisfactorily explained if the total population of free atoms was increased

TABLE 3.8
ORGANIC SOLVENT ENHANCEMENT; THERMAL EFFECT

Total number of combined sample atoms in flame per unit time	Number of free atoms formed in flame	State of atoms	Signal
Aqueous solvent			
10,000	1000	10 excited	S_1 (emission)
		990 unexcited	A_1 (absorption)
Organic solvent			
10,000	1000	50 excited	$5S_1$
		950 unexcited	$(950/990)A_1$

in the flame. If we consider the mechanism of formation of free atoms in the flame, we can see that aqueous and organic solvents behave quite differently. The processes are indicated in Table 3.9.

When an aqueous solvent is used, steps 1 and 2 are endothermic. The process takes energy from the flame and must be forced to take place by the flame. However, when an organic solvent is used, both steps 1 and 2 are exothermic and take place spontaneously and rapidly. This results in a higher efficiency in producing free atoms in the flame. This alternate mechanism is represented numerically in Table 3.10.

The combustibility of the organic solvent increases the

number of excited atoms and neutral atoms. This causes
enhancement of absorption and emission signals. There
must also be a secondary effect of the solvent on the emission signal. The increase in flame temperature must increase
the number of thermally excited atoms. If a transition
element is aspirated into an oxyhydrogen flame, only about
1 atom in 10^6 is excited; the number of neutral atoms in

TABLE 3.9
SOLVENT COMBUSTION MECHANISM

COMBUSTION OF AN AQUEOUS SOLVENT		
step 1	step 2	step 3
ions in $\longrightarrow$ evaporation	$\longrightarrow$ residue	$\longrightarrow$ excited atoms
water leaving a	(dehydrated	(emission)
hydrated	atoms formed)	neutral atoms
residue		(absorption)

COMBUSTION OF AN ORGANIC SOLVENT		
step 1	step 2	step 3
metals in $\longrightarrow$ solvent	$\longrightarrow$ organic	$\longrightarrow$ excited atoms
organic burns	addend	(emission)
solvent	burns	neutral atoms
		(absorption)

such a population is therefore $(10^6 - 1)$. If the number of
excited atoms increased tenfold there would be ten excited
atoms per 10^6. The emission signal would increase tenfold,
but the number of neutral atoms would only decrease to
$(10^6 - 10)$, an insignificant decrease which would cause a
similar decrease in the absorption signal. It therefore seems
conclusive that, if the enhancement of the emission was
caused by a temperature increase, an alternate explanation
would be required for the enhancement of the absorption
signals. However, the fact that organic solvents enhance
both absorption and emission signals strongly supports the

postulate that the enhancement is caused by an increase in the total number of atoms produced in the flame.

Strong supporting evidence was found by Lockyer and co-workers (8). They found that an enhancement took place if mixed organic-aqueous solvents were used. However, if the aqueous and organic solvent was aspirated into

TABLE 3.10
ENHANCEMENT OF ABSORPTION AND EMISSION SIGNALS
BY ORGANIC SOLVENTS

Total number of combined sample atoms in flame per unit time	Number of free atoms formed in flame	State of atoms	Signal
Aqueous solvent			
10,000	1000	10 excited	S_1
		990 unexcited	A_1
Organic solvent			
10,000	2000	20 excited	$2S_1$
		1980 unexcited	$2A_1$

the flame separately, using two burners, there was no enhancement. This indicated that the flame temperature was unimportant but atomization efficiency was dependent on the solvent.

Another explanation proposed for this enhancement is that organic solvents increase the sample feed rate into the flame. This proposal is sound as far as it goes. Provided the flame is not swamped, increased sample feed rate does increase the absorption signal, and sometimes increases the emission signal. The reason is the same as proposed above, that is, there is an increase in the number of atoms formed.

However, the true correlation between sample feed rate and absorption signal depends on the type of burner used. If a total-consumption burner is used, the feed rate is the total rate at which the sample is aspirated into the flame. Although a significant portion of the sample passes completely through the flame without evaporating or decomposing to atoms, it is still considered to be fed into the flame.

On the other hand, if a Lundegardh burner is used, the feed rate is the difference between the rate at which the sample is nebulized and the rate at which the excess sample drips out of the sample barrel. This feed rate is more accurate than that observed with a total-consumption burner. It includes only that sample which is evaporated and reaches the flame in the vapor state. This is a major part of step 1 (Table 3.9). In other words, when Lundegardh burners are used the efficiency of evaporation directly affects sample feed rate and the efficiency of step 1.

We can conclude from these observations that the enhancement effect of organic solvents is probably caused by changes in the combustion pattern of the solvent. Observations on the sample feed rate using Lundegardh burners would indicate that evaporation of the solvent is a very important step in the combustion pattern. This conclusion would of course come as no surprise to combustion experts.

VI. MECHANICAL-FEED TOTAL-CONSUMPTION BURNER (9)

The flame atomizers available commercially are designed primarily with the combustion step in mind. There is no direct control over the feed rate of the sample. Liquids with different viscosities or surface tensions are aspirated and nebulized at different rates. This results in a change in the efficiency of producing neutral atoms from the sample and

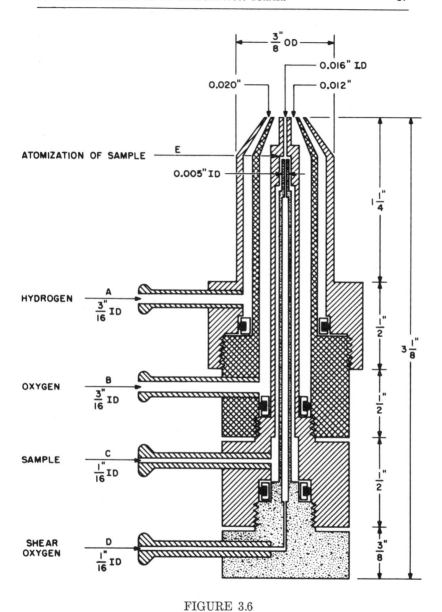

FIGURE 3.6

Schematic Diagram of a Mechanical-Feed Total-Consumption
Burner.

therefore in a change in sensitivity. Furthermore, if a change is made in the flame conditions by varying the fuel, or oxygen flow rate, the sample flow rate is also changed. These complications make interpretation of the effect of variables on absorption and emission data difficult. For example, when organic solvents are used instead of aqueous samples, there is usually an increase in sensitivity. A significant portion of this increase can frequently be ascribed to an increase in sample feed rate. But the increased feed rate may cause overloading of the flame and a decrease in sensitivity. Just how much increase in sensitivity is due to the "combustability" of the organic solvent is therefore a matter of speculation. To answer these and other questions, a mechanical burner was designed (Figure 3.6).

The burner operated as follows. The liquid sample was mechanically displaced into the "sample" part (c) of the burner. The rate of feed was independent of the viscosity, surface tension, and vapor pressure of the solvent; aspiration rate, bore size, and partial clogging of the burner. At the tip of the inlet capillary (E), the liquid sample was sheared off into small drops by high-pressure oxygen. Presumably these drops were similar in size, which, of course, is desirable to attain high combustion efficiency. The small drops were then swept rapidly into the base of the flame.

The function of a burner is to nebulize and atomize the sample. By using the mechanical feed burner, much of the nebulization was done before the flame was reached and a higher atomization efficiency resulted.

A. Optimum Operating Conditions

The ratio of fuel to oxygen was varied over a wide range. Aqueous samples of nickel (10 ppm) were injected into the

burner. The absorption and emission signals were measured
at the various fuel/oxygen ratios. This was repeated using
organic solvents. Optimum operating conditions are shown
in Table 3.11.

TABLE 3-11
Optimum Oxygen-Fuel Pressure (psig) for
Atomic-Absorption and Flame-Emission Signal

	Fuel ratio			
	Atomic abs., max. signal		Flame emis., max. signal	
Solvent	H_2	O_2	H_2	O_2
Aqueous	2.0	0.6^a	3.5	8.0
Organic	0.2^a	0.6^a	0.2^a	2.0

^{a} Minimum reading on gauge.

Unfortunately, the flame conditions were measured in
terms of gas pressure rather than flow rate. Nevertheless,
the results clearly show that the optimum operating conditions for emission and atomic absorption are quite different.
Also, the best flame conditions are different if organic rather
than aqueous solvents are used. These differences can all be
explained in terms of the efficiency of producing neutral
atoms for atomic absorption and excited atoms for emission
flame photometry.

B. Sample Feed Rate

The emission and absorption signals increased with increasing feed rate up to 4 ml/min. This is in contrast to

total-consumption burners for which the optimum feed rate is usually about 1.0 ml/min for aqueous or organic solvents. This increased efficiency was probably the result of nebulization of the sample before entry into the flame. It was concluded from this that, provided atomization can be achieved without swamping the flame, increased feed rate gives an increase in signal.

C. Solvent Viscosity

Solutions of nickel (10 ppm) as nickel naphthenate were made up in various organic solvents. These were fed into a mechanical feed burner, and the absorption and the emission signals were measured. The test was repeated using a Beckman total-consumption burner. Results are shown in Table 3.12.

The effect of viscosity fell into two categories, depending on the type of burner used. When the Beckman aspiration burner was used, there was a tendency for the absorption signal to decrease as viscosity increased. This tendency was less apparent when a correction for sample feed rate was made. For the samples tested, the results were perhaps more noteworthy for their lack of correlation between absorption signal and viscosity. No doubt with highly viscous solvents there is difficulty in aspirating the sample and sensitivity is lost. However, with the solvents tested, other properties seemed to be more important. For example, there were great differences between benzene and toluene, and cyclohexane and methyl cyclohexane, although each of these pairs of compounds is similar physically and chemically. The reasons for these variations have not yet been found.

When the total-force-feed burner was used, the effects of the viscosity of the solvent on the degree of absorption was

TABLE 3.12

ABSORPTION AND EMISSION OF NICKEL 3414-A RESONANCE LINE IN VARIOUS SOLVENTS
(10 PPM N_1)

| Solvent | Forced-feed burner | | Beckman aspiration burner | | Viscosity at 20°C (1000n) |
	Absorption, $I_0 - I_1$	Emission	Total absorption	Absorption corrected for feed rate	
Acetone	14.5	33	15	7.0	3.3
n-Heptane	15.5	40	—	—	4.2
Ethyl acetate	13.0	37	12	7.5	4.5
Methyl alcohol	15	29	9	5.8	5.9
Benzene	16.0	42	2	1.9	6.5
Toluene	15.0	38	16	15.5	7.7
Methyl cyclohexane	16.0	39	20	14.0	7.7
Amyl acetate	13.5	36	—	—	8.0
Cyclohexane	15.0	35	8	7.3	9.3
Carbon tetrachloride	8.0	5	5	4.0	9.6
Ethyl alcohol	15.0	31	6	3.7	12.0
Nitrobenzene	13.5	34	2	1.0	19.8
Isopropanol	15	33	—	—	22.5
Varsol	14.5	30	5	9.3	—
Water	4	4	3	3.0	10.0

very small. Other effects also seem to have been eliminated at the same time. Some slight variation was noted in the absorption signal obtained when combustible solvents were used. This variation was considerably greater when the emission signal was measured; however, it could not be correlated with solvent viscosity.

Upon using noncombustible solvents, water and carbon tetrachloride caused a significant change in both the emission and absorption signal, but this did not appear to be related to viscosity.

D. Effect of Organic Solvents

By using the data provided in Table 3.12, we can clearly see the enhancement effect of organic solvents. Using the mechanical feed burner the organic and the aqueous solvents were fed at the same feed rate, that is, 1 ml/min. The results show a fourfold enhancement in absorption when any of the organic solvents (except CCl_4) were used instead of water. Since the sample feed rate was not a variable in these studies, it could not have been the cause of enhancement. These results support the hypotheses that the combustibility of the organic solvents is a major factor. This is particularly so when it is noted that CCl_4, a noncombustible solvent, is exceptional. A most important practical observation of these studies was that the absorption signal was almost independent of the organic solvent used when a forced-feed burner was used. This should be particularly useful for continuous plant stream analysis, where variation in solvent composition is always a problem with other burners.

VII. FLAME ADAPTERS

Flame adapters are designed to retain neutral atoms in the optical light path. When a normal flame with no adapter is used, the neutral atoms are quickly swept up through the light beam, but when an adapter is used these atoms are physically prevented from doing this. The result is an accumulation of neutral atoms in the light path and therefore in an increase in sensitivity. The first adapter (10) is illustrated in Figure 3.7. Early work showed

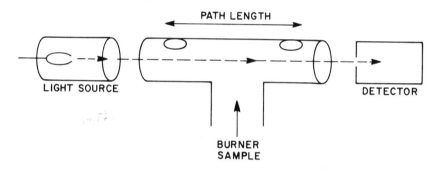

FIGURE 3.7

The T-Piece Flame Adapter.

that the usefulness of these adapters depended on the lifetime of the neutral atoms in the flame. Noble-metal atoms are stable and can be accumulated easily and effectively. Reactive elements such as the alkali metals are unstable and as a result cannot be easily accumulated. Therefore, by using this device, the analytical detection limits of metals such as platinum can be greatly improved. However, for reactive atoms, the sensitivity limits are not greatly improved.

The early design shown in Figure 3.7 was later improved by Fuwa and Vallee (7) and by Koirtyohann and Feldman (11) independently. The latter adapter is shown in Figure 3.8.

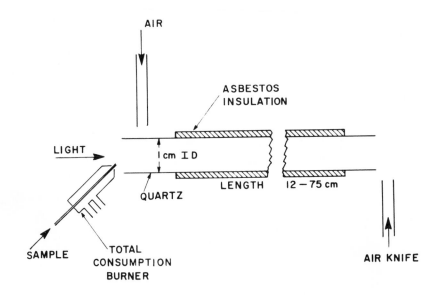

FIGURE 3.8

The Long-Path Flame Adapter [after Koirtyochann and Feldman (11)].

Large increases in sensitivity have been claimed through use of this adapter. It should be particularly useful for samples where high sensitivity is required and only limited amounts of sample is available, such as in medical work.

Further studies on the use of these adapters show that

extensive absorption by the combustion products are sometimes encountered. The degree of absorption varies greatly
with flame conditions. For example, with an oxyhydrogen
flame, changes in the ratio of oxygen to hydrogen caused
considerable variation in the absorption by the flame. A
change from aqueous to organic solvents also changed the
degree of absorption. Further, the absorption by solvent
combustion products is very susceptible to changes in the
oxygen fuel ratio of the flame. However, there were work-
able ranges of flame conditions where analysis could be
carried out reproducibly.

When oxyacetylene flames were examined, it was found
that absorption by the flame products and the solvent-com-
bustion products were even greater than those from oxyhydrogen flames. The most useful application of oxyacetylene flames is for the determination of metals which
form refractory oxides, such as molybdenum. A highly reducing flame is used in these cases. Unfortunately, when
highly reducing flames were used in conjunction with a
flame adapter, absorption as high as 81 per cent by the
flame and solvent combustion products was encountered.
Any absorption by the metal atoms determined was
swamped under these conditions and a loss of sensitivity
resulted.

It can be concluded that, under properly controlled conditions, flame adapters can be used to increase the detection
limits of many metals. However, there may be extensive
absorption by the products of combustion, both from the
flame and the solvent. To get reproducible results, flame
conditions such as fuel-oxygen flow rates and sample feed
rates must be rigidly controlled. In all cases a correction
must be made for this absorption when determining the
absorption by the metal atoms.

VIII. EFFECT OF CHANGING THE SPECTRAL SLIT WIDTH

The spectral width of the lines emitted from a hollow cathode are very narrow (about 0.01 A). In general, the total spectral slit width falling on the detector is greater than this by several orders of magnitude. It is not possible under most circumstances to decrease the mechanical slits enough to prevent any particular portion of such a narrow line from falling on the detector. If the mechanical slits are open at all, the entire emission line falls on the detector.

TABLE 3.13
SENSITIVITY LOSS CAUSED BY NEIGHBORING UNABSORBED LINE

Intensity of initial signal	Intensity of signal after absorption	Sensitivity
Resonance line only, I_0	I_1	$\dfrac{I_0 - I_1}{I_0} = 1\%$
Resonance line and second unabsorbed line, $I_0 + I'_0$	$(I_0 - I_1) + I'_0$	$\dfrac{(I_0 - I_1) + I'_0}{I_0 + I'_0} = 1\%$

Therefore, if we consider only an absorption line emitted from the hollow cathode, the extent of absorption should be independent of slit width. However, in practice this is not the case.

Suppose there is a second emission line with a wavelength very close to the absorption line. If the spectral slit width is wide enough, both lines will fall on the detector. But only the absorption line can be absorbed. This leads to a loss in sensitivity as indicated in Table 3.13.

A. Changes in Sensitivity with Unabsorbable Light Falling on the Detector

It can be seen that even when all the resonance line is absorbed, the signal falling on the detector is only reduced to I'_0. The sensitivity is defined as that quantity which reduces the absorption by 1 per cent. In the first case this is true when $(I_0 - I_1)/I_0 = 1$ per cent. If in the second case $I_0 = I'_0$ and the same quantity of the resonance line was absorbed, the absorbed fraction is $(I_0 - I_1 + I'_0)/(I_0 + I'_0) = 0.5$ per cent. This would result in the procedure being half as sensitive even though the same fraction of I_0 was absorbed.

The same reasoning holds if the unabsorbable light falling on the detector is merely "background" and not a discernible line. This indicates that a narrow slit is generally an advantage and results in increased sensitivity. A illustration is shown in Table 3.14 which gives some supporting data.

It must be noted that the unabsorbable light can emanate from these source. In this case the light may be other iron

TABLE 3.14

Effect of Spectral Slit Width on Sensitivity [4][a]

Mechanical slit width, mm	Spectral slit width, A ($\frac{1}{2}$-wave)	Sensitivity, ppm (1% absorption)
0.015	3.2 (measured)	5
0.05	3.2 (measured)	5
0.1	4.7 (measured)	6
0.4	7.5 (measured)	7
0.6	11.5 (measured)	10
1.0	19.5 (calculated)	50
1.5	29.5 (calculated)	100

[a] Spectral line used, Fe 3719 A.

lines, hollow cathode filler-gas lines, or background continuum. The results shown in Table 3.14 support the validity of the reasoning. However, the extent of sensitivity loss will depend on the total emission spectrum in the immediate vicinity of the absorption line. In cases where this line is remote from other spectral lines wide slits can be tolerated with little loss in sensitivity.

B. Effect of Dispersion on Sensitivity

The effect of changes in dispersion provided by the monochromator is similar in many respects to changes in the spectral slit width. With good dispersion (and narrow slits) radiation which cannot be absorbed may be prevented from falling onto the detector. This allows the maximum sensitivity to be obtained. As before, if the dispersion is inadequate, unabsorbable light falls on the detector and sensitivity is lost. What is considered adequate depends on the emission spectrum in the immediate vicinity of the absorption line. If there is no background or line emission in this vicinity, poor dispersion will not cause a decrease in sensitivity. However, if strong emission is present in the immediate spectral vicinity, high dispersion (and small slits) are required. There is no hard and fast rule to be followed; each absorption line of each metal must be considered on its own merits. The prime requirement is that unabsorbable radiation from the hollow cathode must not be allowed to fall on the detector.

IX. INTERFERENCES

In flame photometry there are three major sources of interference: excitation, radiation, and chemical interference. Each has a counterpart in atomic-absorption spectroscopy, particularly when flame atomizers are used. Their importance is considered below.

A. Excitation Interference

In flame photometry, when the sample is introduced into the flame, the metal atoms become excited. Suppose the sample contains two metals, A and B. It is possible that excited metal A atoms will transfer energy to unexcited metal B atoms. The intensity of emission from metal B would be greater than if no metal A was present in the sample. This type of interference is excitation interference. It is particularly important in alkali metal analysis. With these metals, extensive interference from this source is said to take place.

The counterpart in atomic-absorption spectroscopy is considerably less extensive because only the neutral atoms are involved in the absorption of energy. Frequently, the number of excited atoms in a flame is in the order of 10^{-6} of the total atoms present. Even in the case of the alkali metals, only one atom per thousand is excited and 999 are unexcited. Suppose the emission signal is doubled because of excitation interference. Two atoms per thousand must now be excited and 998 unexcited. The change in the emission signal is 100 per cent, but the absorption signal only changes 0.1 per cent of the total signal. This change would not be detectable on most equipment. For example, in the determination of sodium at the 10-ppm and the 500-ppm levels, no interference was found from 5000 ppm of potassium or lithium.

The lack of interference from excitation effects is one of the inherent advantages that atomic absorption holds over emission procedures.

It should be noted, however, that under conditions of high temperature, e.g., an oxy-hydrogen flame, ionization of alkali metals can take place with a decrease in neutral atom population and a corresponding loss in sensitivity.

B. Radiation Interference

In emission techniques, such as flame photometry or emission spectrography, the intensity of emission from the sample element is measured at some particular wavelength. If another element also emits at the same wavelength, there is a direct additive interference to the measurement of the intensity of this line. The source of this interference is any element or compound that emits at the wavelength being used for measurement. This type of radiation can be a problem in atomic-absorption spectroscopy. As described earlier (Chapter 3, Section I) the wavelength used is the resonance wavelength of the element being determined. The intensity of the unabsorbed signal from the hollow cathode is I_0. After absorption by the sample the signal is I_1. However, in the first simple equipment developed, the emission signal (S) from the atomizer (for example, a flame) at the resonance wavelength also registered on the detector. The latter records a signal equivalent to $(I_0 - I_1) + S$, where S is the emission signal from the flame. The true absorption reading should be $(I_0 - I_1)$, and S in the case is a direct source of error.

There are three principle sources of radiation at this frequency, that is, the broad-background emission from the atomizer, the line emission from other elements in the sample, and most important, the emission by the element being determined at its own frequency.

If the resonance wavelength is less than 2800 A, the intensity of emission from all three sources is usually negligible and no problem arises. At longer wavelengths, background flame emission, and emission from other elements can frequently be somewhat reduced by decreasing slit width. The emission of the resonance line from metal being analyzed cannot be eliminated by decreasing slit width because its wavelength is identical to that used for absorption measurements. Further, its intensity is subject to all the interferences encountered in flame photometry.

Fortunately, this type of interference can be virtually eliminated by using modulated equipment. This process has been described in Chapter 2, Section II, and is so effective in eliminating this serious source of interference that it is difficult to understand why modulated equipment is not always used in atomic-absorption studies.

There is a secondary radiation effect not eliminated with modulation. If the emission from the atomizer is intense, the photomultiplier detector may become overloaded and noisy. This results in a loss in precision, but not necessarily in a loss in accuracy of the determination. When highly incandescent flames, such as reducing oxy-acetylene flames, are used the loss in precision may be high. Instances have been found of this light from the atomizer travelling backward down the sample light path to the face of the hollow cathode. At this interface some reflection takes place, the light now returns in a modulated form by passing through the modulating chopper to the detector, and an error in accuracy can result. The problem is eliminated either by using an electrically chopped system as opposed to a mechanical chopper, or by slanting the hollow cathode face to avoid direct reflection along the light path.

Freedom from radiation interference, when modulated equipment is used, is a major advantage of atomic absorption over emission methods.

C. Chemical Interference

Chemical interference is common to both emission and absorption processes. The cause, as described earlier, is as follows. The extent of absorption depends on how many absorbing atoms are in the light path. For a given concentration of a particular metal, this number depends on the stability of the metal compound in the flame atomizer. If the compound is broken down easily, many neutral metal atoms are produced. If it is broken down with difficulty, only few neutral metal atoms are produced. For a given metal, whenever there is a change in the predominant anion present, we might expect some change in the number of atoms produced and therefore in the extent of absorption. This interference may not be extensive and can be controlled by controlling the predominant anion present. However, this is not always possible.

The problem can sometimes be solved by complexing the metal in the sample, In this fashion, the metal exists as a particular complex no matter what other anions are present. An example of chemical interference and its elimination is shown in Table 3.5.

The results clearly show the variation in absorption obtained when different anions were added to lead nitrate. In practice there is usually no way to be sure which anion is predominant in solution, except of course in repetitive samples. The addition of EDTA was quite effective in this case. Other organic complexing agents should be equally effective with other metals.

1. Matrix Effect

It has been observed that high concentrations (several per cent) of salt result in a decrease in signal. This may be caused by a decrease in the atomizing efficiency of the flame. Suppose a flame has enough energy to decompose 100 μg of salt. If most of this salt is formed by the metal being determined, the efficiency will be high. However, if high concentrations of another salt are present, the flame will use up its energy in decompósing this salt. The efficiency in producing atoms of the element being determined will decrease. Sensitivity decreases and an interference in the analysis results. The problem can be most easily overcome by simple dilution. However, if the concentration of the sample element is too low to permit this, extraction of either that element or the interfering salt may be necessary.

REFERENCES

1. J. W. Robinson, *Anal. Chem.*, **33**, 1226 (1961).
2. M. D. Amos, Aztec Instruments, private communications, March 1965.
3. J. A. Goleb and Y. Yokoyama, *Anal. Chim. Acta*, **30**, 213 (1964).
4. A. C. Menzies, *Anal. Chem.*, **32**, 898 (1960).
5. J. W. Robinson, unpublished work, 1965.
6. A. G. Gaydon, *The Spectroscopy of Flames*, Wiley, New York, 1957.
7. K. Fuwa and B. L. Vallee, *Anal. Chem.*, **35**, 942 (1963).
8. R. Lockyer, J. E. Scott, and S. Slade, *Nature* **189**, 830 (1961).
9. J. W. Robinson and R. J. Harris, *Anal. Chim. Acta*, **26**, 439 (1962).
10. J. W. Robinson, *Anal. Chim. Acta*, **27**, 465 (1962).
11. S. R. Koirtyohann and C. Feldman, *Develop. Appl. Spectry.*, **3**, 180 (1963).

CHAPTER FOUR

Analytical Applications

Atomic-absorption spectroscopy is like all other analytical quantitative procedures in that there is a maximum and minimum to the concentration range of application. The minimum of the range is a function of the limits of detection of the element under optimum conditions. The maximum is extended by using a resonance line with a low coefficient of absorption, but is limited by the ultimate lack of a significant change in the extent of absorption when the sample concentration is increased.

In practice, the upper limit can be extended by three methods. In the first method the sample solution is diluted until the concentration is in a good analytical range. The second method can be applied by using long burners (similar to Walsh's design). By placing the burner perpendicular to the light path rather than along it, much of the flame is taken out of the light path; the number of absorbing atoms is reduced, and there is a reduction in sensitivity. The third method of extending the analytical range to more concentrated solutions is to use an absorption line with a low oscillator strength.

To determine metals present as a major component, any one or all three methods may be applied according to which is the most convenient for the particular sample. Frequently, the best method is to use an absorption line with a low oscillator strength, because this does not involve any extra steps in sample preparation or realignment of equipment.

I. SENSITIVITY LIMITS

The lower limits of the analytical range is determined by the sensitivity limits of the particular metal. For ease of comparison of results by different experimentalists the sensitivity limit has been artificially defined as that concentration which absorbs 1 per cent signal (I_0) under the conditions used. This definition may provide a concentration that is optimistic if the equipment used is somewhat unstable and gives noisy readings. However, using popular commercial equipment these concentrations are generally pessimistic. The signal noise level is usually low enough so

TABLE 4.1

Sensitivity Limits of Various Elements Reported as PPM

1	2	3	4	5	6	7	8	9	10	11	12	13	14	15	16	17	18
Li 0.03	Be 0.2											B 250	C	N	O	F	Ne
Na 0.03	Mg 0.001											Al 0.8	Si 15.	P 100.	S	Cl	A
K 0.03	Ca 0.08	Sc 0.5	Ti 12.0	V 7.0	Cr 0.006	Mn 0.005	Fe 0.1	Co 0.013	Ni 0.01	Cu 0.005	Zn 0.0005	Ga 1.0	Ge	As 1.0	Se 0.5	Br	Kr
Rb 0.1	Sr 0.05	Y 50.	Zr	Nb 250.	Mo 0.5	Tc	Ru 0.25	Rh 0.3	Pd 0.3	Ag 0.05	Cd 0.004	In 0.6	Sn 0.025	Sb 0.1	Te 0.02	I	Xe
Cs 0.15	Ba 3.5	La	Hf	Ta	W	Re 25.	Os	Ir 0.2	Pt 0.7	Au 0.01	Hg 0.5	Tl 0.05	Pb 0.013	Bi 0.1	Po	At	Rn
Fr	Ra	Ac	Th	Pa	U												

that even concentrations lower than those calculated by using the definition can be detected. However, for comparative purposes, the universal use of this definition has provided an unambiguous meaning for reported data. It is highly recommended that future workers in this field continue to report sensitivity limits according to this definition.

The most sensitive limits reported for the different elements are shown in Table 4.1. These data have been obtained by numerous experimentalists under a variety of conditions. No attempt has been made to correlate the sensitivity limits that would have been obtained if only one procedure had been used throughout. In all cases only the most sensitive results have been reported.

Results show that the majority of the metals can be detected at concentrations of less than 1 ppm and that many of them can be detected at the part-per-billion level. Most of the data quoted were obtained using flame atomizers. Although these atomizers are handy and cheap, they are inefficient. It is quite conceivable that sensitivity limits could be improved a thousandfold for all detectable elements if a more efficient means of producing neutral atoms from the sample were used.

II. QUANTITATIVE ANALYSIS

Flame atomizers are used in most equipment. The efficiency of different burners varies appreciably even between burners of the same design. It is therefore necessary to construct calibration curves using standard solutions and conditions. For best results, these standard solutions should be as similar to the sample as possible. This is particularly important with regard to the solvent and the concentration and variety of predominant anion present. A typical set of

calibration curves for the different absorption lines of copper
is shown in Figure 4.1.

In normal routine analysis it is always good practice to
run one or more standard samples with each batch of un-
knowns. This allows corrections to be made for day-to-day
variations in operating conditions. These variations include
changes in sample feed rate caused by partial encrustation

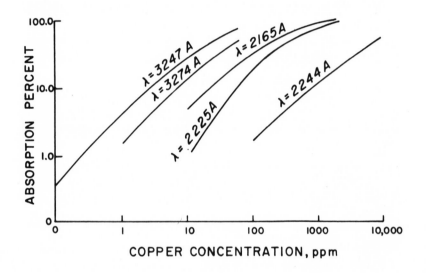

FIGURE 4.1

Calibration Curves for Various Copper Absorption Lines.

of the burner or a change in viscosity of liquid samples
resulting from fluctuations in sample temperature. Unsuspected errors arising from other sources may also be compensated for in this fashion. Recommended analytical conditions and applications for the various metals are shown
below.

III. RECOMMENDED PROCEDURES FOR QUANTITATIVE ANALYSIS

The following are conditions and analytical procedures that have been recommended for use with flame atomizers. By using these conditions, reproducible quantitative results have been obtained by workers in the field. The most suitable conditions for analyzing day-to-day samples can be chosen from those outlined below. In general, the author prefers to use oxyhydrogen or oxyacetylene flames whenever possible because the high flame temperature reduces chemical interference effects. However, other workers (1) prefer to use air instead of oxygen. They contend that, in general, the high temperatures reached by oxygen flames are too hot for producing neutral atoms. It can be anticipated that nitrous oxide flames will make a significant impact on recommended procedures in the near future.

The *sensitivities* quoted are defined as that concentration of solution that will lead to 1 per cent absorption when atomized in a flame. By this definition, all results are measured with the same standard. However, it should be pointed out that these results are generally pessimistic in describing the actual measurable concentration of sample.

It has been suggested (1) that a more realistic detection limit should be quoted when comparing atomic absorption to other analytical techniques used for performing trace-metal determination. The detection limit can be defined in terms of the signal-to-noise ratio of the actual measurement. This means of reporting data is common to a number of analytical fields and is usually quite realistic. However, it is often difficult to reproduce the operating noise levels reported in the literature. For this reason, two people working on the same problem may each produce a signal of the same intensity, but if one is operating at a different noise level than the other, they will report different detection limits.

Therefore, although in practice the reported detection limits must be used with caution, they are useful in comparing atomic absorption with other analytical processes. On the other hand, the sensitivity limits as defined earlier do not suffer from experimental uncertainty. Although the results obtained are probably pessimistic, they do give the worker in the field a firm footing for comparing his data with other atomic-absorption data.

The author wishes to thank the Perkin-Elmer Corporation, and in particular Walter Slavin, for help and suggestions in writing this section and for permission to use their publication *Analytical Methods for Atomic Absorption Spectroscopy (1)*. A considerable portion of the information in the following section is based on data made available through their publication.

Aluminum

Absorption wavelength, A	Sensitivity, ppm	Analytical range, ppm	Ref.
3092	2.0	20–200	(1)
3092	0.8		(2)
3092	1.7	20–200*	(3)
3961	3.*	20–200*	(3)
3082	4.*	20–200*	(3)
3944	5.*	20–200*	(3)
3944	1.0		(4)
2373	10.*	50–200*	(3)
2367	15.*	50–200*	(3)
2575	20.*	50–200*	(3)

* Approximation based on (3).

SPECTRAL SLIT WIDTH: 10 A

FLAME: Highly reducing

Fuel: Acetylene

Oxidant: Oxygen

RECORDED INTERFERENCES: Iron (*3*), chloride (*3*); no interference from Cu, Pb, Mg, Na, PO_4^{3-}, SO_4^{2-} (*3*).

RECORDED SAMPLE TYPES: Steel (*1*)

Analytical Notes

Early research work failed to reveal asborption by aluminum when flame atomizers were used. Strong absorption was obtained using an electrical discharge across a sprayed solution of aluminum (*4*). The equipment was designed for demonstration purposes and was not intended for routine application. The sensitivity limits achieved were 1 ppm at a wavelength of 3944 A.

A similar sensitivity was obtained at the wavelengths 2569 and 2575 A, using flash heating (*5*). This instrument was developed for routine analyses. Samples of tungsten were analyzed in the initial work.

By using his sputtering device, Walsh (*5a*) was able to determine aluminum in zinc.

Later work on flame atomizers (*6*) showed that aluminum could be detected down to 6 ppm in oxyhydrogen flames if the aluminum was in the form of an organometallic compound and if it was in an organic solvent. This can be achieved by complexing the aluminum and extracting with methyl isopropyl ketone.

Further developments (1) showed that aluminum could be determined in steel by dissolving the sample in HCl, evaporating the solution *almost* to dryness, and redissolving in ethyl alcohol. A strongly reducing air-acetylene flame was used.

More recently, aluminum in aqueous samples has been successfully determined (3). An improved burner was developed for this work. Slight interference was noted from high concentration of iron and chloride. This problem was eliminated by preparing standards similar in iron and chloride content to the samples. The problem may be less important using modulated equipment.

Sensitivity in nitrous oxide-acetylene flame was 1 ppm (7).

Antimony

Absorption wavelength, A	Sensitivity, ppm	Analytical range, ppm	Ref.
2175	0.5	10–100	(1)
2068	0.5		(8)
2311	1.2		(8)
2176	0.1 with flame adapter		(9)

SPECTRAL SLIT WIDTH: 7 A

FLAME: Reducing

Fuel: Acetylene

Oxidant: Air, oxygen

RECORDED INTERFERENCES: The sensitivity is dependent on spectral slit width.

RECORDED SAMPLE TYPES: No data

Arsenic

Absorption wavelength, A	Sensitivity, ppm	Analytical range, ppm	Ref.
1937	3	20–200	(1)
1890	1		(10)
1972			(10)

SPECTRAL SLIT WIDTH: 0.7 A; high background makes high resolution necessary.

FLAME: Oxidizing

Fuel: Acetylene

Oxidant: Air, oxygen

RECORDED INTERFERENCES: No data

RECORDED SAMPLE TYPES: No data

Analytical Notes

The sensitivity is very dependent on slit width.

Barium

Absorption wavelength, A	Sensitivity, ppm	Analytical range, ppm	Ref.
5536	5.0	20–200	(1)

SPECTRAL SLIT WIDTH: 40 A

FLAME: Highly reducing

Fuel: Acetylene, hydrogen

Oxidant: Air, oxygen

RECORDED INTERFERENCES: Aluminum, phosphorus; no interference from Ca, Sr, Mg.

RECORDED SAMPLE TYPES: Alkaline earth carbonate (*1*), lube oils (*1*), petroleum products (*11*).

Analytical Notes

ALKALINE EARTH CARBONATES (*1*):   The sample is dissolved in HCl and the solution analyzed directly.

WORN LUBE OILS AND PETROLEUM MATERIALS (*1, 11*):
The sample is diluted with *n*-heptane and analyzed directly.
   Standards for calibration curves can be made by dissolving a suitable quantity of barium cyclohexanebutyrate (NBS standard 1051) in 3 ml of xylene plus 5 ml 2-ethyl hexanoic acid. The mixture is dissolved in lube oil. This is the base solution and may be diluted to the required volume with *n*-heptane.

Beryllium

Absorption wavelength, A	Sensitivity, ppm	Analytical range, ppm	Ref.
2349	0.2	No data	(1)

SPECTRAL SLIT WIDTH: 3 A

FLAME: Highly reducing

Fuel: Acetylene

Oxidant: Oxygen

RECORDED INTERFERENCES: No data

RECORDED SAMPLE TYPES: No data

Analytical Notes

Under the recommended flame conditions the absorption signal is noisy. To diminish this effect, the hollow cathode should be operated at the highest current levels possible without impairing the life of the source.

Sensitivity in nitrous oxide-acetylene flame 0.02 ppm (7).

Bismuth

Absorption wavelength, A	Sensitivity, ppm	Analytical range, ppm	Ref.
2231	1.0	10–100	(1)
3068	1.0		(12)
2062	1.0		(12)
2228	4.0		(12)
2231*	0.1 using flame adapter		(9)

* There is absorption by hydroxyl of the 3068-A line.

SPECTRAL SLIT WIDTH: 2 A

FLAME: Oxidizing or reducing

Fuel: Hydrogen, acetylene

Oxidant: Air, oxygen

RECORDED INTERFERENCES: Sensitivity is dependent on spectral slit width and on lamp current.

RECORDED SAMPLE TYPES: Urine (*13*)

Analytical Notes

It has been claimed that the sensitivity is increased in low temperature flames (*13*).

URINE SAMPLES: The sample is adjusted to a pH between 2.5 and 4.0. The bismuth is complexed with 1 per cent ammonium dithiocarbamate solution and extracted with 10 ml of methyl isobutyl ketone (*13*). The calibration curve is made up from bismuth in the same solvent.

Boron

No systematic studies have been made on boron. Absorption has been observed at the following wavelengths using reducing air-acetylene flames.

Absorption wavelength, A	Sensitivity, ppm	Analytical range, ppm	Ref.
2497	250	No data	(1)

Analytical Notes

Boron has been detected using flash heating (5). The procedure was not developed for routine analysis.
Sensitivity in nitrous oxide-acetylene flame 90 ppm (7).

Cadmium

Absorption wavelength, A	Sensitivity, ppm	Analytical range, ppm	Ref.
2288	0.04	0.5–5.0	(1)
3261	20		(12)
2288	0.001 with flame adapter		(9)
2288	0.0004 with flame adapter		(14)

SPECTRAL SLIT WIDTH: 7 A

FLAME: Oxidizing

Fuel: Hydrogen, acetylene

Oxidant: Air, oxygen

RECORDED INTERFERENCES: No data

RECORDED SAMPLE TYPES: Urine (1); zirconium and zirconium alloys (15)

Analytical Notes

It is claimed that the sensitivity is increased when low-temperature flames are used (13).

URINE: Cadmium can be determined directly in urine samples (*13*). The sample should be stabilized by adding 1 ml of glacial acetic acid per 100 ml of sample.

Calcium

Absorption wavelength, A	Sensitivity, ppm	Analytical range, ppm	Ref.
4227	0.1	2–20	(1)
2399	20		(12)

SPECTRAL SLIT WIDTH: 40-A max

FLAME: Highly reducing

Fuel: Acetylene, hydrogen

Oxidant: Oxygen, air

The preferred flame is rich oxyacetylene. This flame reduces anionic interferences.

RECORDED INTERFERENCES: Beryllium, zirconium, phosphorus, vanadium, or aluminum (*12, 16*). The interference is removed by using a reducing flame and by adding either lanthanum or strontium to form a 1 per cent solution. Alternatively, EDTA may be added to form a 1 per cent solution. Sodium and potassium enhance the signal. Any error can be eliminated by adding an excess of sodium or potassium to the standard solution and samples (*17*). Perchlorate enhances the absorption (*18*).

RECORDED SAMPLE TYPES: Animal tissue (*1*), saliva (*1*), blood serum (*19, 20*), urine (*19*), cement (*1*), lubricating oils (*1*), petroleum products (*11*), soils (*21*), plants (*17*), bone ash (*22*), beer (*23*).

Analytical Notes

A sputtering device has been used to study calcium absorption (*24*). It was found that 1.0 μg could be detected using the 4227-A resonance line.

It is claimed that the analytical sensitivity is increased by running the source at higher currents (*25*).

Anionic interferences are reduced by using rich air-acetylene flames. In low-temperature flames the sensitivity is reduced and chemical interferences are increased.

The flame profile is quite sharp. Therefore, to get reproducible results it is important to use the same part of the flame for all measurements.

ANIMAL TISSUE (*1*): The sample is ashed by burning overnight. The ashes are dissolved in HCl and the solution analyzed directly.

PETROLEUM MATERIALS AND LUBE OILS (*1, 11*): The samples are diluted with *n*-heptane and analyzed directly.

PLANT SAMPLES (*17*): About 2 g of sample is digested in 3.5 ml $HClO_4$ plus 0.5 ml H_2SO_4 and 15 ml HNO_3. This is digested on a hot plate until fumes of H_2SO_4 come off, indicating that the $HClO_4$ has been eliminated. The residue is redissolved in a H_2SO_4 solution. Lanthanum is added until a concentration of 1 per cent is reached. The volume is adjusted to bring the calcium to a suitable concentration. The sample is now ready for analysis.

In his studies, David (*17*) found that Na and K enhanced the signal and that Fe and Mg suppressed the signal. This can be compensated for by using similar standard samples for calibration purposes. He found that Al and PO_4^{3-} interfered. However, by adding La to the solution, any interference from Al, PO_4^{3-}, SiO_2, SO_4^{2-}, Na, and K was eliminated (*21*).

SALIVA (*26*): Add lanthanum solution to provide a final 1 per cent solution. Run directly.

BLOOD (*19, 20*): Add lanthanum solution to provide a final 1 per cent solution. Run directly.

URINE (*19*): Analyze directly. Stabilize the sample by adding 1 ml glacial acetic acid per 100 ml of sample.

SOILS (*21*): Extract 10 g of soil with a *N* NH_4Cl solution Add lanthanum to provide a final 1 per cent solution. Analyze directly.

It is important that calibration curves be made from standard samples similar to the final solution of the samples being analyzed. It is especially important that solvent and the major components be similar.

Cesium

Absorption wavelength, A	Sensitivity, ppm	Analytical range, ppm	Ref.
8521	0.15	No data	(12)
4556	20		(12)

SPECTRAL SLIT WIDTH: 8521 A   40 A

4556 A   8 A

FLAME: Oxidizing

Fuel: Acetylene, hydrogen, coal gas

Oxidant: Air, oxygen

RECORDED INTERFERENCES: No data

RECORDED SAMPLE TYPES: No data

Analytical Notes

Studies by Gatehouse and Willis (*12*) showed that the sensitivity was 0.15 ppm in air-coal gas flames and 0.5 in air-acetylene flames. They found that, if a discharge lamp was used as the source, it should be run at a low current to reduce self-absorption of the resonance line by the lamp itself. Failure to do this reduces sensitivity and leads to inaccurate results.

They further found that in the low-temperature flames used, other alkali metals which may be present in the sample changed the population of the ground-state cesium atoms, and an interference resulted. The effect can be compensated for by preparing calibration curves from standard solutions containing concentrations of interfering alkali metals similar to those present in the samples.

Chromium

Absorption wavelength, A	Sensitivity, ppm	Analytical range, ppm	Ref.
3579	0.15	2–20	(1)
4254	0.5		(8)
3579	0.006		(27)

SPECTRAL SLIT WIDTH: 0.7 A

FLAME: Highly reducing

Fuel: Acetylene, hydrogen

Oxidant: Oxygen, air

The degree of absorption is very sensitive to flame conditions.

RECORDED INTERFERENCES: No data

RECORDED SAMPLE TYPES: Lube oils (*1*), petroleum products (*11*), urine (*1*), blood plasma (*22*)

Analytical Notes

A sensitivity of 0.006 ppm has been obtained (*27*) by using a long-path flame adapter. It was found that better sensitivity was obtained using air-hydrogen rather than oxyhydrogen flames. Also, the noise level of the signal was high. The final method proposed used an extract of chromium in methyl isobutyl ketone.

URINE: The sample was acidified to preserve it, and centrifuged if necessary. It was analyzed directly.

LUBE OILS AND PETROLEUM PRODUCTS (*1, 11*):   The sample was diluted with *n*-heptane and analyzed without further preparation. Calibration curves should be obtained from standards similar to the samples, particularly with respect to the solvent and major components.

Cobalt

Absorption wavelength, A	Sensitivity, ppm	Analytical range, ppm	Ref.
2407	0.5	4–40	(1)
3527	3.0	30–300	(12)
3454	4.0		(12)
2425	0.4		(12)
2521	0.6		(12)
2425	0.013 with flame adapter		(14)

SPECTRAL SLIT WIDTH:　3 A max

FLAME:　Oxidizing

Fuel:　Hydrogen, acetylene, liquid petroleum gas

Oxidant:　Air, oxygen

The air-liquid petroleum flame has lower flame absorption than air acetylene.

RECORDED INTERFERENCES:　No data

RECORDED SAMPLE TYPES:　Urine (*1*)

Analytical Notes

The sensitivity decreases as the slit width increases. Also, the signal-noise level increases with increasing slit width (*29*). Sensitivity also decreases with high lamp currents.

URINE (*1*):　The samples are stabilized by adding 1 ml glacial acetic acid per 100 ml of sample. Analysis can be performed directly. None of the components usually present in these samples interferes with the absorption.

Copper

Absorption wavelength, A	Sensitivity, ppm	Analytical range, ppm	Ref.
3247.5	0.1	2–20	(1)
3274.0	0.2		(8)
2178.9	0.4		(8)
2165.1	0.7		(8)
2181.7	0.9		(8)
2225.7	2.		(8)
2024	4.		(8)
2492.1	9		(8)
2244.3	22		(8)
2441.6	55		(8)
3247.5	0.005 with flame adapter		(9)
3247.5	0.007		(14)

SPECTRAL SLIT WIDTH: 7 A

FLAME: Oxidizing

Fuel: Hydrogen, acetylene

Oxidant: Oxygen, air

RECORDED INTERFERENCES: The sensitivity is dependent on slit width.

RECORDED SAMPLE TYPES: Aluminum alloys (*15*), copper ores (*30*), alloys (*15*), fertilizers (*31*), lube oils (*1*), petroleum products (*11*), crude oil (*32*), plant materials (*31*), soils (*31*), urine (*1*), butter (*33*), butter oil (*33*), silicate rocks, blood serum, milk (*34*), wines (*35*), beer (*23*), electroplating solutions (*36*).

Analytical Notes

Numerous absorption lines are available for copper absorption (*37*). By selecting a suitable absorption wavelength, copper samples can be analyzed over a very wide range of concentration.

If necessary, copper can be extracted from aqueous solutions by complexing with 1 per cent ammonium pyrrolidine dithiocarbamate and extracting with methyl isobutyl ketone (*31*).

PETROLEUM MATERIALS (*38*): Dilute with *n*-heptane and analyze the solution directly.

COPPER OR ALUMINUM ALLOYS (*15*): The sample is dissolved in 50 per cent (v/v) HNO_3. SiO_2 is eliminated by treating with HF. Excess HF is displaced by fuming with H_2SO_4. The residue is diluted and the solution is ready for analysis.

FERTILIZER (*31*): The sample is dissolved in HCl. It is then diluted to a suitable volume, and the solution is analyzed.

SOILS (*31*): The sample is decomposed using a mixture of HNO_3, HF, and $HClO_4$. The residue is dissolved in 5 per cent $HClO_4$ solution, diluted to a suitable volume, and analyzed.

Ores (*30*) : The sample is partially decomposed using a mixture of HF and HNO_3. The copper dissolves in the acid. After complete extraction, the solution is separated off and diluted to a suitable volume. The solution is analyzed.

Plant Samples (*31*) : The sample is decomposed with a mixture of 17 ml HNO_3 plus 3 ml $HClO_4$. The volume is reduced to about 2 ml and then diluted with distilled water to a suitable volume. The solution is analyzed.

Urine Samples (*1*) : The samples are stabilized by adding about 1 per cent of their volume of glacial acetic acid. The sample may be analyzed directly.

It is important to use calibration curves made from standards similar to the solvent and the other major components present.

Gallium

Absorption wavelength, A	Sensitivity, ppm	Analytical range, ppm	Ref.
2944	4	2–20	(1)
2874	4		(12)
4172	5		(12)
4033	7		(12)

The sensitivity is dependent on lamp current.

Spectral Slit Width : 20 A

Flame: Oxidizing

Fuel: Acetylene

Oxidant: Air, oxygen

RECORDED INTERFERENCES: No data

RECORDED SAMPLE TYPES: No data

Analytical Notes

Gallium melts at a low temperature. Hollow cathode lamps should therefore be run at a low current.

Germanium

Sensitivity in nitrous oxide-acetylene flame is 5.5 ppm (7).

Gold

Absorption wavelength, A	Sensitivity, ppm	Analytical range, ppm	Ref.
2428	0.1	2–20	(1)
2428	0.01	0.1–0.5	(39)
2676	1.3		(12)

SPECTRAL SLIT WIDTH: 20 A

FLAME: Reducing

Fuel: Hydrogen, acetylene, propane-butane

Oxidant: Air, oxygen

RECORDED INTERFERENCES: No interference from Cr, Mo, Ga, As, Sb, Sn, Se, Te, Ge (39).

RECORDED SAMPLE TYPES: Urine (*1*), noble metals (*40*), cyanide waste (*39*).

Analytical Notes

URINE SAMPLES: Preserve the sample by adding 1 ml glacial acetic acid per 100 ml of sample. Analyze the samples directly.

Hafnium

Sensitivity in nitrous oxide-acetylene flame is 12 ppm (*7*).

Indium

Absorption wavelength, A	Sensitivity, ppm	Analytical range, ppm	Ref.
3039.7	1	5–50	(1)
3256.1	0.6		(8)
2560.2	0.8		(8)
4101.8	1.0		(8)

SPECTRAL SLIT WIDTH: 1 A

FLAME: Oxidizing or reducing

Fuel: Hydrogen, acetylene

Oxidant: Air, oxygen

RECORDED INTERFERENCES: No data

RECORDED SAMPLE TYPES: No data

Iron

Absorption wavelength, A	Sensitivity, ppm	Analytical range, ppm	Ref.
2483.3	0.3	2–20	(1)
3719.9	1.0	5–50	(1)
2488.1	0.2		(1)
2522.8	0.2		(41)
2719.0	0.4		(41)
3020.6	0.5		(41)
2527.4	0.6		(41)
2720.9	0.9		(41)
2966.9	1.2		(41)
3859.9	2.0		(41)
3440.6	2.8		(41)

SPECTRAL SLIT WIDTH: 2 A max

FLAME: Oxidizing

Fuel: Hydrogen, acetylene

Oxidant: Air, oxygen

RECORDED INTERFERENCES: No data

RECORDED SAMPLE TYPES: Cement (*1*), fertilizers (*41*), lube oils (*1*), petroleum products (*32*), plants (*41*), plating solutions (*1*), soils (*41*), beer (*23*).

Analytical Notes

Sensitivity is decreased at high lamp currents and with increased spectral slit width.

Hollow cathodes filled with neon give better analytical sensitivity than lamps filled with argon. However, neon lamps "clean-up" quicker and therefore have a shorter life.

CEMENT (1): Dissolve in HCl, filter if necessary. Dilute to a suitable volume and analyze.

FERTILIZER (41): Dissolve in HCl, evaporate to dryness. Redissolve in dilute HCl, and analyze.

LUBE OILS (37, 38): Dilute threefold with n-heptane. Samples with high iron concentrations should be analyzed using the resonance line at 3720 A. Low concentrations can be determined using the 2483-A line.

PLANT SAMPLES (41): Weigh out about 2.0 g of sample. Decompose, using a mixture of 17 ml HNO_3 plus 3 ml $HClO_4$. After the sample has decomposed, evaporate on a hot plate to a volume of about 2 ml. Redissolve in water. Dilute to a suitable volume and analyze.

CHROMIUM PLATING SOLUTIONS (1): Dilute with water and analyze.

SOILS (41): Decompose with a mixture of HNO_3 and $HClO_4$. Add HF to eliminate silicates and evaporate to dryness. Dilute to a suitable volume with 5 per cent $HClO_4$.

It is important in all cases to use calibration curves derived from standards similar to the final sample solution, particularly with regard to the solvent and major components present.

Lead

Absorption wavelength, A	Sensitivity, ppm	Analytical range, ppm	Ref.
2170	0.5	4–40	(1)
2833	0.7	5–50	(12)
2833	0.5	1–12	(42)
2614	50.0		(12)
4058	150.0		(12)
2833	0.013 with T-piece adapter		(16)
2833	0.02 with flame adapter		(9)

SPECTRAL SLIT WIDTH: 2 A

FLAME: Slightly oxidizing

Fuel: Acetylene, hydrogen

Oxidant: Oxygen

RECORDED INTERFERENCES: No interference from Ag, Ba, Bi, Cd, Ce, Co, Cr, Cu, Fe, Hg, K, La, Li, Mg, Mn, Na, Ni, Sn, Sr, Th, Zn. Interferences noted from Al, Be, Th, Zr (*43*) when low-temperature flames and unmodulated equipment was used. No interference was noted from Al, Be, Th, Zr when oxyhydrogen flames and modulated equipment were used (*16*). PO_4^{3-}, Cl^-, CO_3^{2-}, I^-, SO_4^{2-}, and F^- caused interference (compare to NO_3^-). These interferences were removed by adding 1 g EDTA per 100 ml of sample (*16*). High Ca^{2+} interfered (*42*).

RECORDED SAMPLE TYPES: Copper alloys (*15*, *44*), gasoline (*45*), lube oils (*1*), steel (*15*, *44*), urine (*13*), wines (*35*), petroleum materials (*11*).

It is claimed that neon-filled lead hollow cathodes give better sensitivity. With argon lamps, unabsorbed argon lines from the hollow cathode overlap with the lead 2833-A line. This is avoided when neon is used (*46*).

Analytical Notes

Lead can be extracted into organic solvents by several methods. Dagnal and West (*43*) found extracting as diethyldithiocarbamate at pH 7 into ethyl acetate gave better analytical sensitivity than if the lead was extracted as the 8-hydroxyquinoline into methyl isobutyl ketone. Other complexing agents which have been used in conjunction with atomic absorption include dithizone and ammonium pyrrolidine dithiocarbamate. In each case the complex was extracted with hexanone.

The flame-absorption profile is quite sharp. For reproducible results the same part of the flame must be used for all measurements.

GASOLINE (*45*): Dilute 1:10 with *n*-octane. Analyze directly. Use tetraethyllead, or a mixture of tetraethyllead and tetramethyllead as the standard.

WORN LUBE OILS (*1*): Dilute with *n*-heptane. Analyze directly.

PETROLEUM MATERIALS (*11*): Dilute with *n*-heptane. Analyze directly. Lead cyclohexanebutyrate can be used for making standard solutions; it is dissolved in 3 ml xylene plus 5 ml ethyl hexanoic acid. The mixture is dissolved in lube oil and used as the stock solution.

COPPER BASE ALLOYS (*15*): Dissolve in HNO_3. Boil to drive off nitrous fumes. Dilute to a suitable volume and analyze the solution.

STEEL (*15*): Dissolve in HCl; oxidize by adding HNO_3 dropwise. Drive off SiO_2 with HF or filter. Dilute with water to a suitable volume and analyze.

URINE: Take 50 ml of sample and adjust to pH 2.8 with HCl. Complex with 1 ml ammonium pyrrolidine dithiocarbamate. Extract with 10 ml of methyl isobutyl ketone. Analyze the extract.

Lithium

Absorption wavelength, A	Sensitivity, ppm	Analytical range, ppm	Ref.
6708	0.07	1–10	(1)
3233	15.0		(12)

SPECTRAL SLIT WIDTH: 40 A

FLAME: Oxidizing

   Fuel: Acetylene, hydrogen, coal gas, liquid petroleum gas

   Oxidant: Oxygen, air

Low-temperature flames such as air-acetylene increase sensitivity by reducing the extent of ionization of this easily ionized metal.

RECORDED INTERFERENCES: No data

RECORDED SAMPLE TYPES: Isotope analysis (47)

Magnesium

Absorption wavelength, A	Sensitivity, ppm	Analytical range, ppm	Ref.
2852	0.02	0.2–2.0	(1)
2796	5.0		(12)
2025	2.0		(12)
2852	0.001 with flame adapter		(9)
2852	0.005 with flame adapter		(14)

SPECTRAL SLIT WIDTH: 20 A

FLAME: Reducing

Fuel: Acetylene, hydrogen

Oxidant: Oxygen, air

The absorption by magnesium is very sensitive to changes in the height of the light path through the flame. For reproducible results this must be carefully controlled.

RECORDED INTERFERENCES: High concentration of aluminum or phosphates interfere. This interference can be removed by adding lanthanum, strontium, or EDTA (1 per cent) plus sodium. If Ca is present, PO_4^{3-} interference is increased by adding EDTA but not by adding La or Sr. Anionic interferences are high in air-liquid petroleum flames.

RECORDED SAMPLE TYPES: Aluminum alloys (*48*), cast iron (*1*), nickel and nickel alloys (*49*), cement (*1*), animal tissue (*50*), blood serum (*51, 52*), foods and fecal material (*53*), bone ash (*22*), urine (*19, 53*), plants (*1*), soils (*21*).

Analytical Notes

Analytical sensitivity decreases with increased lamp current.

ANIMAL TISSUE (*50*): The sample is dissolved in concentrated HNO_3. Nitrous fumes are driven off, and the sample is diluted to a suitable volume and analyzed.

CAST IRON (*1*): The sample is dissolved in HCl and oxidized with HNO_3 to eliminate carbon. If the silica content is high, it is removed by adding HF and boiling. The sample is evaporated to a small volume and redissolved in HCl. Sr or La are added to eliminate interference from Al or PO_4^{3-}. The final solution is now analyzed.

CEMENT (*1*): The sample is dissolved in HCl, diulted to a suitable volume, and analyzed.

FECAL MATERIAL AND FOODS (*53*): The sample is ashed overnight in a muffle furnace. The residue is redissolved in HCl, diluted, and analyzed.

NICKEL ALLOYS (*49*): The sample is dissolved in HNO_3. Nitrous fumes are driven off. The sample is diluted and analyzed.

PLANT SAMPLES (*54*): Approximately 2 g of sample is decomposed in a mixture of 3.5 ml $HClO_4$, 0.5 ml H_2SO_4, and 15 ml HNO_3, using an electric heater. The solution is evaporated until fumes of H_2SO_4 come off. The sample is redissolved, filtered, and diluted to a suitable volume with 1 per cent H_2SO_4. It is then analyzed.

BLOOD SAMPLES (*51*): Take 0.1 ml of sample, dilute to 5.0 ml with water, analyze directly.

SOILS (*21*): Extract 10 g soil with N ammonium chloride. Dilute and àdd Sr to make a final solution of 1500 ppm Sr. Analyze the solution.

URINE (*19, 53*): Dilute to a suitable volume with water. Because of the wide variation in Mg content, a rough check may be necessary before the correct dilution is found. Analyze the diluted sample.

Manganese

Absorption wavelength, A	Sensitivity, ppm	Analytical range, ppm	Ref.
2795	0.08	2–20	(1)
2798	0.01		(1)
2801	0.15		(41)
4031	0.8		(41)
2795	0.005 with flame adapter		(9)

SPECTRAL SLIT WIDTH: 3 A for maximum sensitivity; at 20 A the sensitivity is reduced by 50 per cent because the 2975-A line is not resolved from the 2801-A line.

FLAME: Oxidizing

Fuel: Hydrogen, oxygen

Oxidant: Oxygen, air

RECORDED INTERFERENCES: Anionic

RECORDED SAMPLE TYPES: Copper base alloys (*15*), fertilizer (*41, 55*), plants (*41*), soils (*41, 55*), steel (*15*), blood plasma (*22*).

Analytical Notes

Analytical sensitivity is somewhat dependent on lamp current.

COPPER AND IRON ALLOYS (*15*): Dissolve in 50 per cent HCl, then oxidize by dropwise addition of HNO_3. Filter off SiO_2 if necessary. Redissolve and analyze the solution.

FERTILIZER (*41, 55*): Dissolve the fertilizer in HCl. Evaporate to dryness and redissolve in 0.5 N HCl. Dilute to a suitable volume and analyze the solution.

PLANTS (*41*): 2 g of plant material is digested in an acid mixture consisting of 3.5 ml $HClO_4$, 0.5 ml H_2SO_4, and 15 ml HNO_3 until fumes of H_2SO_4 are given off. The residue is redissolved in H_2SO_4. Any SiO_2 present is filtered off. The filtrate is diluted to a suitable volume and analyzed.

Soils (*41, 55*):   The soil is digested in a mixture of HNO_3, $HClO_4$, and HF. After driving off all the SiO_2 with the HF, the solution is evaporated to fumes and then redissolved in 5 per cent $HClO_4$. It is diluted to a suitable volume and analyzed. Calibration curves should be made from standards containing 5 per cent $HClO_4$.

Mercury

Absorption wavelength, A	Sensitivity, ppm	Analytical range, ppm	Ref.
2357	10	20–200	(1)
2537	0.5 with flame adapter		(56)
1849	Not detected		(10)
1849	<10		(13)

Spectral Slit Width: 20 A

Flame: Oxidizing

Fuel: Hydrogen, acetylene

Oxidant: Air, oxygen

Recorded Interferences: No data

Recorded Sample Types: Urine (*13*)

Analytical Notes

Mercury can be complexed in acid solutions with ammonium pyrrolidine dithiocarbamate (*13*) or dithizone and extracted into methyl *n*-amyl ketone.

URINE SAMPLES (*13*): Acidify to pH 2.5–4.0, complex with ammonium pyrrolidine dithiocarbamate, and extract with 10 ml of methyl *n*-amyl ketone.

Molybdenum

Absorption wavelength, A	Sensitivity, ppm	Analytical range, ppm	Ref.
3133	0.5	1–100	(7)
3170	1.7		(57)
3798	2.0		(57)
3194	2.0		(57)
3864	2.5		(57)
3903	3.0		(57)
3158	4.0		(57)
3209	10.		(57)
3112	2.0		(57)

SPECTRAL SLIT WIDTH: 2 A

FLAME: Highly reducing oxy-acetylene or air-acetylene only. Very sensitive to changes in flame conditions.

Fuel: Acetylene

Oxidant: Air, oxygen

RECORDED INTERFERENCES: No data

RECORDED SAMPLE TYPES: Fertilizer (*58*), steel (*58*), blood plasma (*22*).

Analytical Notes

FERTILIZER (58): Extract the molybdenum by boiling with concentrated HNO_3 plus HCl. Dilute with water, filter, and add $AlCl_3$ to provide a final concentration of 2000 ppm Al. Analyze the solution.

STEEL (58): Dissolve in 15 ml HNO_3 plus 30 ml HCl. Dilute, filter, and add $AlCl_3$ to give a final concentration of 2000 ppm Al. Analyze the solution.

NOTE: It is important that the standards used for preparing calibration curves contain 2000 ppm Al.

Nickel

Absorption wavelength, A	Sensitivity, ppm	Analytical range, ppm	Ref.
2320.0	0.2	2–20	(1)
3414.8	3.0	30–300	(1)
2310	0.4		(8)
2345.5	2.0		(8)
3524.5	2.5		(8)
3050.8	3.5		(8)
3002.5	6.0		(8)
3461.7	6.0		(8)
2320	0.01 with flame adapter		(9)
2311	0.016 with flame adapter		(14)

SPECTRAL SLIT WIDTH: 1.0 A; sensitivity is very dependent on slit width.

FLAME: Oxidizing

Fuel: Hydrogen, acetylene

Oxidant: Air, oxygen

RECORDED INTERFERENCES: No interference from Cr, Mn, W, Cu, Co, V, Mo, Al, K (*59*).

RECORDED SAMPLE TYPES: Petroleum feed stocks (*32*), petroleum materials (*11*), urine (*13*), steel (*59*), electroplating solution (*36*).

Analytical Notes

PETROLEUM MATERIALS (*11, 38*):   Dilute with lube oils and analyze. Calibration curves can be obtained using nickel cyclohexanebutyrate dissolved in 3 ml xylene plus 5 ml of 2-ethyl hexanoic acid. The solution is diluted with lube oil.

For high sensitivity the absorption line at 2320 A is used for measuring purposes. For lower sensitivity the 3414-A absorption line is preferred because it is less noisy.

URINE (*13*):   The nickel is complexed with ammonium pyrrolidine dithiocarbamate and extracted with methyl isobutyl ketone. The extract is analyzed directly.

STEEL (*59*):   Dissolve in acid, filter if necessary, and analyze the solution. No interference was noted from 30 per cent Cr, 20 per cent Mn, 20 per cent W, 10 per cent Cu, 10 per cent Co, 5 per cent V, Mo, or Al.

Niobium

No systematic studies have been made on niobium. Absorption at the following wavelengths has been observed using very rich oxyacetylene flames.

Absorption wavelength, A	Sensitivity, ppm	Analytical range, ppm	Ref.
4059	250	No data	(60)
4080	250		(60)
4101	250		(60)

Palladium

Absorption wavelength, A	Sensitivity, ppm	Analytical range, ppm	Ref.
2474.4	1.0	10–100	(1)
2447.9	0.3		(8)
2763.1	1.0		(8)

SPECTRAL SLIT WIDTH: 2.0 A

FLAME: Reducing

Fuel: Acetylene, hydrogen, propane-butane

Oxidant: Oxygen, air

RECORDED INTERFERENCES: Dependent on lamp current

RECORDED SAMPLE TYPES: Noble metals (40)

Platinum

Absorption wavelength, A	Sensitivity, ppm	Analytical range, ppm	Ref.
2659	8.0	10–100	(1)
2147.7	2.0		(8)

Sensitivity is dependent on lamp current and slit width.

SPECTRAL SLIT WIDTH: 2.0 A

FLAME: Reducing

Fuel: Hydrogen, acetylene, propane-butane

Oxidant: Oxygen, air

RECORDED INTERFERENCES: Interferences have been noted in low-temperature flames.

RECORDED SAMPLE TYPES: Noble metals (*40*)

Potassium

Absorption wavelength, A	Sensitivity, ppm	Analytical range, ppm	Ref.
7665	0.1	1–10	(1)
4044	5.0		(12)

SPECTRAL SLIT WIDTH: 40 A

FLAME: Oxidizing; low-temperature reducing flames increase sensitivity by reducing the extent of ionization of this easily ionized metal (*2*).

Fuel: Hydrogen, acetylene, coal gas

Oxidant: Air, oxygen

RECORDED INTERFERENCES: Calcium (*61*). High concentration of sodium, lithium, and cesium enhance the absorption of potassium (*19*). In air-acetylene flame; high concentrations of sodium interfere. In high-temperature flames, high concentrations of Na, Li, and Cs may interfere (*1*).

RECORDED SAMPLE TYPES: Blood serum (*62*), cement (*1*), plant materials (*1, 55*), soils (*21*), bone ash (*22*), beer (*23*).

Analytical Notes

BLOOD (*62*):   Dilute 0.1 ml of blood to 5.0 ml with water. Analyze the solution.

CEMENT (*1*):   Dissolve 1 g of cement in 5 ml of HCl. Add water to make up to about 50 ml. Filter, wash, and dilute the filtrate to a suitable volume. Analyze the solution.

PLANT SAMPLES (*1, 55*):   Digest about 0.4 g of sample in 17 ml HNO_3 (conc) plus 3 ml $HClO_4$. Evaporate on an electric hot plate and reduce the volume to about 2 ml. Dilute to a suitable volume with water. Analyze the solution.

SOIL EXTRACTS (*21*):   Extract 10 g of soil with N ammonium chloride. Separate the extract and dilute to a suitable volume with water. Analyze the extract.

Rhenium

No systematic studies have been carried out. Absorption at the following wavelengths has been observed using a highly reducing oxyacetylene flame.

Absorption wavelength, A	Sensitivity, ppm	Analytical range, ppm	Ref.
3452	50	No data	(63)
3461	25		(63)
3465	25		(63)

Rhodium

Absorption wavelength, A	Sensitivity, ppm	Analytical range, ppm	Ref.
3434.9	0.3	4–40	(1)
3692	5.0		(8)
3503			(64)
3397			(64)
3658			(64)
3701			(64)

Sensitivity is very dependent on lamp current.

SPECTRAL SLIT WIDTH: 3 A

FLAME: Highly reducing

Fuel: Hydrogen, acetylene, propane-butane

Oxidant: Air, oxygen

RECORDED INTERFERENCES: Numerous interferences have been reported using a propane-butane air flame (*64*). These have not been confirmed; and may not exist in high-temperature flames.

RECORDED SAMPLE TYPES: Noble metals (*40*)

Rubidium

Absorption wavelength, A	Sensitivity, ppm	Analytical range, ppm	Ref.
7800	0.2	2–20	(1)
4202	10.		

SPECTRAL SLIT WIDTH: 40 A

FLAME: Oxidizing; low-temperature flames (coal gas-air) increase the sensitivity to 0.1 ppm.

Fuel: Hydrogen, acetylene, coal gas

Oxidant: Air, oxygen

RECORDED INTERFERENCES: High concentration of other alkali metals change the concentration of rubidium in the flame. Addition of a large quantity of another alkali metal to the sample standardizes these interferences.

RECORDED SAMPLE TYPES: No data

Ruthenium

No systematic studies have been made on ruthenium. Absorption has been observed in highly reducing air-acetylene flame at the following wavelengths.

Absorption wavelength, A	Sensitivity, ppm	Analytical range, ppm	Ref.
3498.9	0.25	No data	(8)
3728.0	0.25		(8)

Scandium

No systematic study has been made on scandium. Absorption has been observed using rich oxyacetylene flames and a continuous source (*63*).

Absorption wavelength, A	Sensitivity, ppm	Analytical range, ppm	Ref.
3907	5	No data	(63)
3912	5		(63)
4020	5		(63)
4024	5		(63)
3270	10		(63)
3274	10		(63)
3256	50		(63)
4054	50		(63)
4082	50		(63)
3933	100		(63)

Selenium

Absorption wavelength, A	Sensitivity, ppm	Analytical range, ppm	Ref.
1961	5	10–100	(1)
1961	0.5		(10)
2040	5	10–100	(10)

SPECTRAL SLIT WIDTH: 7 A

FLAME: Reducing

Fuel: Acetylene

Oxidant: Air

RECORDED INTERFERENCES: High concentration of copper

RECORDED SAMPLE TYPES: Copper, copper alloys (*65*).

Silicon

No systematic studies have been made on silicon. Absorption has been observed at the following wavelength using a highly reducing oxyacetylene flame.

Absorption wavelength, A	Sensitivity, ppm	Analytical range, ppm	Ref.
2516.1	15	No data	(1)

Sensitivity in nitrous oxide-acetylene flame is 10 ppm (*7*).

Silver

Absorption wavelength, A	Sensitivity, ppm	Analytical range, ppm	Ref.
3281	0.1	2–20	(1)
3383	0.15		(12)
3281		0.01–0.1	(66)

SPECTRAL SLIT WIDTH: 7 A

FLAME: Oxidizing

Fuel: Hydrogen, acetylene, coal gas

Oxidant: Oxygen, air.

Low-temperature flames increase sensitivity.

RECORDED INTERFERENCES: IO_3^-, WO_3^-, MnO_4^-, Th (*66*)
No interference from Zn, Mg, Cu, Mn, Ni, Cr, Ti.

RECORDED SAMPLE TYPES: Worn lube oils (*1*), lead, lead sulfide concentrates (*67, 68*), petroleum products (*11*), urine (*1*), aluminum alloys (*69, 70*), Noble metals (*40*).

Analytical Notes

WORN LUBE OILS (1) AND PETROLEUM MATERIALS (*11*): The sample is diluted with *n*-heptane and the mixture analyzed directly.

Calibration curves can be made using silver cyclohexane-butyrate (NBS Standard 1068) as the standard. Weigh 0.129 g of dried standard into 2 ml of xylene and 4 ml of 2-ethylhexylamine. When it clears, add 2 ml of ethyl hexanoic acid. The mixture is diluted with lube oil to 100 g. This contains 500 ppm Ag and acts as the stock solution.

PbS CONCENTRATES (*67, 68*):   Dissolve 4 g of sample in 100 ml 10 *N* HCl. Heat and add 5 ml 16 *N* HNO_3. Evaporate to 50 ml. Dilute to a suitable volume. The final solution should be saturated with lead. Any lead chloride crystals in the solution should be allowed to remain, and the supernatant liquid should be used for analysis.

The standards used for calibration should also be saturated with lead chloride.

URINE (1): Add 1 ml of glacial acetic acid to stabilize the sample. Analyze directly. Several readings should be taken. Water should be run through the burner between each aspiration of the sample.

Sodium

Absorption wavelength, A	Sensitivity, ppm	Analytical range, ppm	Ref.
5890	0.03	0.5–10	(71)
3320	5.0		(71)

SPECTRAL SLIT WIDTH: 40 A For high sensitivity this must be reduced to about 3 A to separate the more sensitive 5890-A resonance line from the sodium doublet line at 5895 A.

FLAME: Oxidizing

Fuel: Hydrogen, acetylene, coal gas

Oxidant: Oxygen, air

Low-temperature flames increase sensitivity by reducing the extent of ionization of this easily ionized metal.

RECORDED INTERFERENCES: Calcium (61). High concentrations of other alkali metals may reduce sensitivity by ionizing the sodium. However, 5000 ppm of K or Li had no effect in oxyhydrogen flames (71). Interference from calcium was noted (61) when unmodulated equipment was used. However, using modulated equipment, no interference from high concentrations of calcium were observed (1).

RECORDED SAMPLE TYPES: Blood serum (*62*), mercury amalgam (*1*), cement (*1*), worn lubricating oils (*1*), petroleum products (*11*), fluorescent phosphors (*72*), soils (*21*), plants (*55*), silicates (*1*), bone ash (*22*), beer (*23*).

Analytical Notes

BLOOD (*62*):   Dilute 0.1 ml of blood to 5.0 ml and analyze the mixture.

CEMENT (*1*):   Dissolve 1 g of sample in 20 ml of water plus 5 ml HCl (conc). Dilute to 50 ml with water and digest. Filter, then wash and dilute the filtrate to a suitable volume. Analyze the solution.

LUBE OILS AND PETROLEUM MATERIALS (*1, 11*):   Dilute the sample to a suitable volume with *n*-heptane and analyze the mixture.

Calibration curves can be made up from standard solutions using sodium cyclohexanebutyrate as the standard. A suitable weight is dissolved in 3 ml xylene plus 5 ml 2-ethyl hexanoic acid. The mixture is diluted to 100 g with lube oil. This solution acts as the stock solution.

PLANTS (*55*):   About 1 g of sample is decomposed with 17 ml HNO_3 (conc) plus 3 ml $HClO_4$. The mixture is heated over an electric hot plate and the volume reduced to about 2 ml. It is then filtered if necessary and diluted to a suitable volume with water. The solution is then analyzed.

SOILS (*21*):   Extract about 10 g of soil with *N* ammonium chloride to a final volume of about 200 ml. Dilute with water if necessary. Analyze the extract.

Strontium

Absorption wavelength, A	Sensitivity, ppm	Analytical range, ppm	Ref.
4607	0.05	2–20	(57)
4078	3.5		(12)
4607	0.1 with flame adapter		(9)

SPECTRAL SLIT WIDTH: 13 A or less

FLAME: Highly reducing

Fuel: Hydrogen, acetylene

Oxidant: Air, oxygen

The proposed flame is oxyacetylene. The degree of absorption is sensitive to flame conditions.

RECORDED INTERFERENCES: No systematic study has yet been made, but the interferences are probably similar to those found for calcium. As a precaution, lanthanum may be added.

Other alkaline earths do not interfere. However, interference may be expected from Al, SiO_2, PO_4^{3-}, SO_4^{2-}, oxalate, and protein (*1*). David (*60*) suggests that these interferences may be overcome by using the method of addition.

RECORDED SAMPLE TYPES: Alkaline earth carbonates (*1*), plant material (*60*), soils (*60*).

Analytical Notes

Analytical sensitivity is best at the lower parts of the flame (*57*). Also the sensitivity is affected by the ratio of air to acetylene used in the flame (*57*).

ALKALINE EARTH CARBONATES (*1*):   Dissolve in water and dilute to a suitable volume. Analyze the solution.

PLANT MATERIALS (*60*):   Ignite the sample in a muffle furnace at 500°C for 4 hr. Dissolve about 0.4 g of ash in 5 ml 6 *N* HCl. Evaporate to dryness, redissolve in HCl, and evaporate to dryness again. Dissolve in 10 ml 0.1 *N* HCl, filter, wash, and dilute. Pass through 50 ml of Deacidite FF (acetate form) anion-exchange resin. Wash with 0.1 *N* acetic acid. Discard the first 9 ml and collect the remainder. Analyze by the method of addition.

SOILS (*60*):   Extract 10 g of soil with 200 ml of *N* ammonium chloride. Pass through a Deacidite FF (acetate) anion-exchange column and treat as described above.

Tantalum

Sensitivity in nitrous oxide-acetylene flame is 15 ppm (*7*).

Thallium

Absorption wavelength, A	Sensitivity, ppm	Analytical range, ppm	Ref.
3775.7	3.0	20–200	(1)
2767.8	1.0		(8)
2379.7	2.0		(8)
2767.8	0.05 with flame adapter		(9)

SPECTRAL SLIT WIDTH: 7 A

FLAME: Oxidizing

Fuel: Hydrogen, acetylene

Oxidant: Air, oxygen

RECORDED INTERFERENCES: No data

RECORDED SAMPLE TYPES: Urine (1), blood serum (1)

Tin

Absorption wavelength, A	Sensitivity, ppm	Analytical range, ppm	Ref.
2863	5	25–200	(1)
2863	0.025		(73)

SPECTRAL SLIT WIDTH: 5 A

FLAME: Highly reducing

Fuel: Acetylene, hydrogen

Oxidant: Air, oxygen

RECORDED INTERFERENCES: Silica, phosphate, pyrophosphates

RECORDED SAMPLE TYPES: Copper alloys (1), hydrogen peroxide stabilizer (73)

Analytical Notes

Tin hollow cathode lamps frequently emit a high background. A small spectral slit width should therefore be used.

The analytical sensitivity is decreased at high lamp currents. Further, tin is easily volatilized. High lamp currents therefore shorten the life of these lamps; thus tin hollow cathodes should be run at low current conditions.

COPPER BASE ALLOYS (1):   Heat a suitable sample in HCl (conc). Dissolve by adding HNO$_3$ (conc) dropwise until solution is complete. Boil to remove nitrous fumes. Dilute to a suitable volume and analyze.

HYDROGEN PEROXIDE STABILIZER (73):   Dilute the sample to contain less than 47 per cent H$_2$O$_2$ to avoid explosion hazards. Analyze the solution directly.

The absorption wavelength used was 2863 A. Because H$_2$O$_2$ absorbs at this wavelength, it is necessary to use standards similar to the samples. The source of tin may be sodium stannate.

Inject the sample by mechanical displacement into a Beckman burner. Direct the flame down a long path absorption tube. Use modulated equipment.

An enhancement may be found when nitrate is added to the solution. Suppression of absorption may be observed in high concentrations of phosphate and pyrophosphate. No interference is normally found at the levels encountered in these samples. The sensitivity limit is about 50 ppm.

Titanium

Absorption wavelength, A	Sensitivity, ppm	Analytical range, ppm	Ref.
3653	12	No data	(74)
3643	12		(74)
3999	16		(74)
3635	16		(74)
3342	20		(74)
3371	50		(74)

SPECTRAL SLIT WIDTH: 9 A

FLAME: Highly reducing oxyacetylene flames

Fuel: Acetylene

Oxidant: Oxygen

RECORDED INTERFERENCES: No data

RECORDED SAMPLE TYPES: No data
Sensitivity in nitrous oxide-acetylene flame is 2 ppm (7).

Tungsten

No systematic studies have been made on tungsten. Absorption has been observed at 4008 A in highly reducing oxyacetylene flames. The sensitivity was 250 ppm (75). Sensitivity in nitrous oxide-acetylene flame is 17 ppm (7).

Vanadium

Absorption wavelength, A	Sensitivity, ppm	Analytical range, ppm	Ref.
3184	7	No data	(74)
4379	100		(74)

SPECTRAL SLIT WIDTH: 40 A

FLAME: Highly reducing oxy-acetylene flames

Fuel: Acetylene, cyanogen

Oxidant: Oxygen

RECORDED INTERFERENCES: No data

RECORDED SAMPLE TYPES: No data
Sensitivity in nitrous oxide-acetylene flame is 2 ppm (7).

Yttrium

No systematic studies have been made on yttrium. Absorption at the following wavelengths has been observed using very rich oxyacetylene flames.

Absorption wavelength, A	Sensitivity, ppm	Analytical range, ppm	Ref.
4077	50	No data	(63)
4102	100		(63)
4128	100		(63)
4143	100		(63)

Zinc

Absorption wavelength, A	Sensitivity, ppm	Analytical range, ppm	Ref.
2138	0.05	0.5–5.0	(1)
3076	150.		(12)
2138	0.0005 with flame adapter		(9)
2138	0.0006 with flame adapter		(14)

SPECTRAL SLIT WIDTH: 20 A

FLAME: Oxidizing

Fuel: Hydrogen, acetylene

Oxidant: Air, oxygen

The sensitivity increases with low-temperature flames. Air-acetylene flames absorb at this wavelength and a correction must be applied.

RECORDED INTERFERENCES: High concentration of silicon. No interference from K, Na, Mg, Co, Cu, Ni, Sr, Mn, Fe, Cr, Al, Au, Mo, Cl⁻, NO_3^-, ClO_4^-, SO_4^{2-}, PO_4^{3-}, (*76*).

RECORDED SAMPLE TYPES: Aluminum alloys (*15*), metallurgical alloys (*78*), animal tissue (*1*), copper alloys (*15*), fertilizers (*55*), plants (*1, 55*), soils (*55*), urine (*13*), zirconium alloys (*15*), silicate rocks, wines (*35*), electroplating solution (*36*).

Analytical Notes

The analytical sensitivity of zinc is very good. Usually the sample can be determined directly in aqueous solution. However, zinc can be extracted from an aqueous solution at pH 2.5–5.0. For a 10 ml sample add 1 per cent aqueous ammonium pyrrolidine dithiocarbamate. Extract the complex with 10 ml methyl isobutyl ketone.

ALUMINUM BASE ALLOYS (*15*): Dissolve a suitable sample in 5 ml HCl (conc). Complete solution by adding H_2O_2 dropwise. If the silicon content of the sample is high, add HF plus a few drops of HNO_3 and 2 ml of H_2SO_4. Evaporate to fumes of H_2SO_4 to remove excess HF. Redissolve the residue in water. Dilute to a suitable volume and analyze the solution.

METALLURGICAL SAMPLES (*77*): Dissolve a suitable sample in HCl (conc). Complete solution by the dropwise addition of HNO₃. If silica is present, filter it off, or volatilize it with HF. Dilute the solution to a suitable volume. Analyze the solution.

ANIMAL TISSUE (*78*): Ash the tissue in a muffle furnace at 600°C overnight. Dissolve a suitable quantity of ash in 3 N HCl. Dilute to a suitable volume with 0.36 N HCl solution. Analyze the solution. Calibration curves should be derived from samples made up in 0.36 N HCl solution.

FERTILIZER (*5*): Dissolve a suitable sample in 3 N HCl. Evaporate to dryness, redissolve in 0.5 N HCl, and dilute with water to a suitable volume. Analyze the solution.

PLANTS (*1, 55*): Digest a suitable sample in 17 ml HNO₃ (conc) plus 3 ml HClO₄. Evaporate on an electric hot plate to about 2 ml. Dilute to a suitable volume with 10 per cent HClO₄ solution. Analyze the solution. The calibration curves should be obtained from standards prepared in 10 per cent HClO₄ solution.

SOIL EXTRACT (*55*): Digest about 2 g of soil in a mixture of HNO₃ and HClO₄. Add sufficient HF to volatilize any silica present. Evaporate to dryness. Redissolve the residue in 5 per cent HClO₄ solution. Dilute to a suitable volume. Analyze the solution.

AVAILABLE ZINC (*55*): Zinc in soil may be determined by extracting the soil with 1 per cent EDTA solution. Filter the extract, wash thoroughly, dilute the filtrate to a suitable volume, and analyze.

URINE (*13*): Stabilize the sample by adding 1 ml glacial acetic acid to every 100 ml of sample. Analyze directly.

WINE (*35*):   Ash a suitable sample. Redissolve the ash in HCl and analyze the solution.

ZIRCONIUM BASE (*15*):   Dissolve about 2 g of sample by dropwise addition of HF. Add a few drops of HNO_3 to clear the solution and 10 ml H_2SO_4. Displace excess HF by evaporating until fumes of H_2SO_4 appear. Add 10 ml HNO_3; and dilute to a suitable volume (about 100 ml). Analyze the solution.

Zirconium

Preliminary studies indicate that zirconium can be determined by its interference effect on the absorption of calcium (*16*). Sensitivity in nitrous oxide-acetylene flame is 9 ppm (*7*).

IV. COMMERCIAL EQUIPMENT

The cost of commercial equipment ranges from $4500 to $7000. Installation costs are minimal although adequate ventilation is essential. Commercial equipment needs only to be plugged into an electrical outlet (115 volts) to be in operating condition. The cost of operating for routine analysis is very small. Day-to-day requirements include a cylinder of fuel and oxygen or air, and a supply of hollow cathodes. Sealed hollow cathodes cost between $75 and $125, depending on the metal involved and the manufacturer.

Hollow cathodes in which the cathode is demountable are not commercially available. However, for the research worker or the laboratory which encounters a multitude of different metals to analyze, this type of hollow cathode can be built without too much difficulty by following the directions of Koirtyohann and Feldman (9).

A. Installation

When metals are aspirated into flames, the fumes from the flames are highly toxic. It is extremely important that adequate ventilation be provided. This can be done either by putting the whole instrument into a hood, or by placing a small exhaust immediately above the flame. This exhaust should be powered with a motor-driven fan. It is important that this safety factor be observed. Many metals are cumulative poisons. Operations may suffer severe damage before they are ever aware of any hazard. Adequate ventilation is easy to install and eliminates this danger.

Commercial equipment is shown in Figures 4.2 to 4.5. The various types of commercial equipment available are typified by the models described below.

B. Aztec Techtron Model AA3

The design of this instrument was based on Walsh's original work. It was developed by the Division of Chemical Physics of the Commonwealth Scientific and Industrial Research Organization, Australia. The detection limits of 35 elements have been discussed by Gatehouse and Willis (12), who used this instrument for their research work.

It is very simple in construction. Each major component can be easily identified, a useful asset for teaching purposes. The optics are single beam and the monochromator is a grating 50×50 mm² with 600 lines per mm. The instrument is electrically modulated and is therefore free

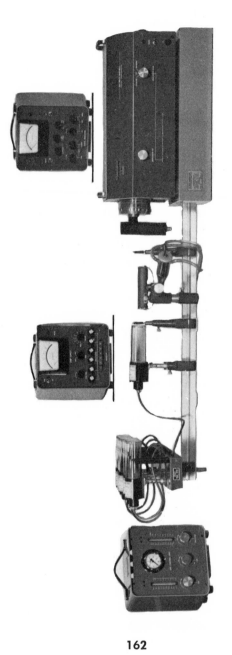

FIGURE 4.2

Aztec Techtron Model AA3.

from radiation interferences. The system is mounted on an optical bench with ample space for inserting a long-path flame adapter.

The use of single-beam optics requires that the source be stable before absorption readings can be taken. If this is not so, the signal drifts steadily as the source warms up, and it is difficult to measure the degree of absorption.

Warm-up periods for hollow cathode sources are usually about 20 min. To avoid delay when lamps are changed, for example, for analyzing different elements, the instrument is fitted with a rack which holds a total of six lamps. These lamps can all be switched on if necessary, and are ready for use at any time without an extra warm-up period.

The basic instrument costs $4900. Extra attachments, including scale expansion and recorder increase the price to about $6000.

As described in the Perkin-Elmer Model 303, the scale-expansion attachment increases the sensitivity which can be obtained if the noise level of the signal is low. An added advantage of this instrument is that it can be converted for use in atomic fluorescence. The extra attachment costs about $500.

C. Beckman Attachments

The Beckman Instrument Company has announced the availability of atomic-absorption attachments for its DB, DU, and DU2 spectrophotometer. Of course, the DU, DU2, and DB instruments can be used for flame photometry and ultraviolet absorption (solution) work. The atomic-absorption attachment extends the usefulness of these machines.

Each atomic-absorption attachment uses single-beam optics. The attachments are fitted with a multipass system,

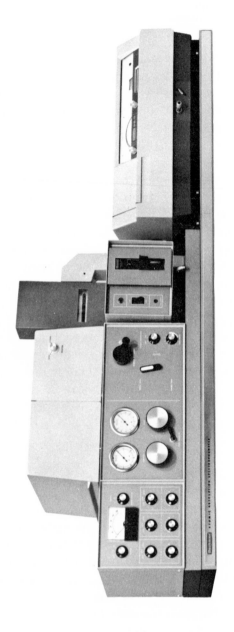

FIGURE 4.3

Beckman Atomic-Absorption Spectrometer.

which allows the light to traverse the flame three times; this usually leads to an enhancement of signal.

A new laminar-flow burner has also been designed for these attachments. It is basically the same as the Lundegardh burner (Fig. 2.9). The sample is injected into a hollow "barrel" which leads into the flame atomizer. With this instrument, the barrel is heated, thus speeding up evaporation of the solvent before the sample reaches the flame. An improvement in atomizer efficiency results. A complete instrument is illustrated in Figure 4.3.

The attachment to the DB utilizes a mechanical chopping device for modulating the equipment. However, the DU and DU2 spectrophotometer both measure dc light, and the atomic-absorption attachment is therefore unmodulated for these instruments. As described earlier, results obtained on unmodulated equipment are subject to radiation interferences from the flame, the burning solvent, and the sample metal itself if it emits at this wavelength. The problem can be reduced by using calibration curves derived from standards as similar as possible to the sample.

The cost of the DB attachment is about $2500; the DU and DU2 attachment cost about $2100. The burner costs an extra $585 to $685, depending on the model.

D. Jarrel Ash Model 82.362

Figure 4.4 shows the Jarrel Ash model 82.362, which can be used for both atomic-absorption and flame photometry and therefore enjoys some advantages of versatility. The atomizer consists of three Beckman total consumption burners in tandem along the light path. The monochromator is a grating with 1180 lines per mm. The source and detector are electrically modulated.

It is a single beam-instrument. The multipass system is designed into the optics. With a set of mirrors, the light beam traverses the flame five times, each time at a different height in the flame. This results in an increase in sensi-

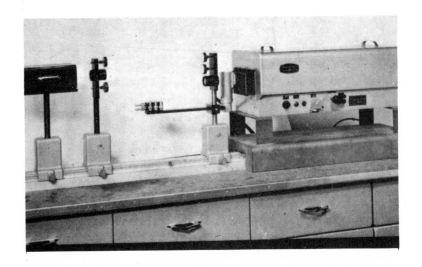

FIGURE 4.4

Jarrel Ash Atomic-Absorption Spectrometer.

tivity which is frequently significant. However, this does not hold for all metals, particularly those that have sharp absorption flame profiles and absorb very little in the upper parts of the flame.

Recent pronouncements from Jarrel Ash herald the first multichannel atomizer, designed to analyze several elements simultaneously.

The cost of the model 82.362 is about $5900. The cost

of gas regulators and recorders bring the price to about $7100.

A useful accessory available on this instrument is an eight-speed scanning device. The instrument is particularly useful for development and research work.

E. Perkin-Elmer Model 303

This instrument is well-suited for routine analysis. It is modulated by a mechanical chopper, and therefore analytical results obtained on this instrument are free of radiation interferences. An illustration is shown in Figure 4.5.

It is the only double-beam instrument commercially available. This feature reduces the effect of variations of light intensity from the source. In the double-beam system, the *ratio* of the sample and reference beams is measured. This greatly reduces the necessity for the absolute value of the light intensity to stay constant over extended periods of time.

The source housing is designed to use hollow cathodes or Osram lamps. The resolution of the optics is adequate for most conventional applications. The readout system is a needle-dial which indicates the degree of imbalance when absorption by the sample takes place. By rotating the control, the needle may be balanced and the percentage absorption by the sample read off the dial directly.

A scale-expansion unit is available. This is used to increase the sensitivity of the detection and readout system. It is useful for increasing sensitivity when the noise level of the signal is low. By using this device, detection limits, which are significantly better than those quoted as sensi-

FIGURE 4.5

Perkin-Elmer Model 303.

tivity limits, may frequently be reached. However, with the detection limit the noise level of the signal is the limiting factor. In many cases, but not always, better detection limits can be attained. The usefulness of this attachment depends on the particular sample and on the particular conditions of the instrument and atomizer used in the analysis.

The burner is similar to the one illustrated in Figure 2.9. It is suitable for burning air-acetylene flames, but is unsafe to use for oxy-acetylene flames.

The space provided for the burner is sufficient for the burner designed for the instrument, or for a total aspiration burner. However, there is insufficient space for a long-path flame adapter (9, 14). There is sufficient space to insert a T-piece adapter (4) if desired. If this is done, steps should be taken to protect the optics, preferably by covering the light path portholes with quartz, and using an air knife across the exits of the T piece.

The cost of the Model 303 instrument is between $6000 and $7500, depending on the number of extra accessories included.

F. MicroTek-Unicam SP290 Atomic Absorption Spectrophotometer

This instrument is designed for use as an atomic absorption spectrometer or a flame photometer. It is lamp modulated and uses single beam optics. Figure 4.6 illustrates the instrument.

Hollow cathodes are held in a turret holder which enables three lamps to be continuously in readiness. The monochromator is a littrow prism with a spectral range from 8500A to 2000A. The burner is premixed with a de-

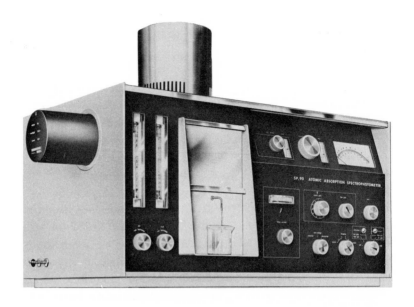

FIGURE 4.6

MicroTek-Unicam Atomic Absorption Spectrometer SP 90

tachable slot head. Three burner heads are available. Burner height is adjustable with a rack and pinion. A feature of the instrument is an automatic sample changer for routine operation. The cost, without recorder, is less than $3500.

G. Hollow Cathodes

None of the commercial equipment listed above includes hollow cathodes in its price. The price of these sources varies with the manufacturer and the particular metal. One hundred dollars each will serve as an estimate, but this should be checked with the supplier.

REFERENCES

1. Analytical Methods for Atomic Absorption Spectroscopy, Perkin-Elmer Corp., Norwalk, Conn., 1964.

2. C. K. Coogan, J. D. Morrison, A. Walsh, and J. K. Wilmhurst, *Nature,* **200,** 319, 4904 (1963).

3. M. D. Amos and P. E. Thomas, *Anal. Chim. Acta,* **32,** 139 (1965).

4. J. W. Robinson, *Anal. Chim. Acta,* **27,** 465 (1962).

5. L. S. Nelson and N. A. Kuebler, *Spectrochim. Acta,* **19,** 781 (1963).

5a. A. Walsh, L.S.U. Intern. Symp. Modern Methods of Analytical Chemistry, January, 1962.

6. C. L. Chakrabarte, G. R. Lyles, and F. B. Dowling, *Anal. Chim. Acta,* **29,** 484 (1963).

7. M. D. Amos, Aztec Instruments, private communications, March, 1965.

8. J. E. Allan, *Spectrochim. Acta,* **18,** 259 (1962).

9. S. R. Koirtyohann and C. Feldman, *Develop. Appl. Spectry.,* **3,** 180 (1963).

10. D. J. David, 4th Australian Spectroscopy Conference, 1964.

11. Analytical Standards for Trace Elements in Petroleum Products, *Natl. Bur. Stds. (U.S.), Monograph* **54,** Oct. 1962.

12. B. M. Gatehouse and J. B. Willis, *Spectrochim. Acta,* **17,** 710 (1961).

13. J. B. Willis, *Anal. Chem.,* **34,** 614 (1962).

14. K. Fuwa and B. L. Vallee, *Anal. Chem.,* **35,** 942 (1963).

15. W. T. Elwell and J. A. F. Gidley, *Atomic Absorption Spectroscopy,* Pergamon, London, 1962.

16. J. W. Robinson, unpublished work, 1965.

17. D. J. David, *Analyst,* September **1959,** 536.

18. J. H. Gibson, W. E. L. Grossman, and W. D. Cooke, 10th Detroit Anachem Conference, October 1962.

19. J. B. Willis, *Anal. Chem.,* **33,** 556 (1961).

20. J. B. Willis, *Spectrochim. Acta,* **16,** 259 (1960).

21. D. J. David, *Analyst,* **85,** 495 (1960).

22. D. C. Manning, *Perkin-Elmer Corp., Newsletter, No. 11,* March 1963.

23. S. W. Fry, *Perkin-Elmer Corp. Newsletter,* Vol. 3.10, 1964.

24. J. A. Goleb and J. K. Brody, *Anal. Chim. Acta,* **28,** 457 (1963).

25. T. Takeuchi and M. Suzuki, *Talanta,* **11,** 1391 (1964).

26. E. Newbrun, *Nature,* **192,** 1182 (1961).

27. R. Lockyer, J. E. Scott, and S. Slade, *Nature,* **189**, 830 (1961).

28. K. Fuwa and B. L. Vallee, *Anal. Chem.,* **35**, 942 (1963).

29. P. Herman and W. Lang, *Arch. Eisenhuettenw.,* **E-10**, 643 (1962).

30. A. Strasheim, F. W. E. Strelow, and L. R. P. Butler, *J. S. African Chem. Inst.,* **13**, 73 (1960).

31. J. E. Allan, *Spectrochim. Acta,* **17**, 467 (1961).

32. R. C. Barras, Pittsburgh Conference on Analytical Chemistry and Applied Spectroscopy, March 1963.

33. J. B. Willis, *Australian J. Dairy Technol.,* **1964**, 70.

34. *Perkin-Elmer Corp. Newsletter, 21,* March 1963.

35. P. B. Zeeman and L. R. P. Butler, *Appl. Spectry.,* **16**, 120 (1962).

36. C. M. Whittington and J. B. Willis, *Plating,* August (1964).

37. J. C. Devaney and F. Brech, Pittsburgh Conference on Analytical Chemistry and Applied Spectroscopy, March 1962.

38. R. C. Barrass, *Jarrel Ash Newsletter,* 13 (1962).

39. F. N. E. Strelow, E. C. Feast, P. M. Mathews, C. J. C. Bothma, and C. R. Van Zyl, *Anal. Chem.,* in press.

40. R. Lockyer and G. E. Hames, *Analyst,* **84**, 385 (1959).

41. J. E. Allan, *Spectrochim. Acta,* **10**, 800 (1959).

42. A. Strasheim, E. Norval, and L. R. P. Butler, *J. S. African Chem. Inst.,* **17**, 55 (1964).

43. R. M. Dagnal and T. S. West, *Talanta,* **11**, 1553 (1964).

44. W. T. Elwell and J. A. F. Gidley, *Anal. Chim. Acta,* **24**, 71 (1961).

45. J. W. Robinson, *Anal. Chim. Acta,* **24**, 451 (1961).

46. W. Slavin and D. Manning, *Appl. Spectry.,* in press.

47. J. A. Goleb and Y. Yokoyama, *Anal. Chim. Acta,* **30**, 213 (1946).

48. F. J. Wallace, *Analyst,* April **1963**, 259.

49. T. R. Andrews and P. N. R. Nichols, *Analyst,* **87**, 25 (1962).

50. C. B. Belcher and H. M. Bray, *Anal. Chim. Acta,* **26**, 322 (1962).

51. J. B. Willis, *Nature,* **184**, 186 (1959).

52. J. B. Willis, *Spectrochim. Acta,* **16**, 273 (1960).

53. J. B. Dawson and F. W. Heaton, *Biochem. J.,* **80**, 99 (1961).

54. J. E. Allan, *Analyst,* **83**, 466 (1958).

55. J. E. Allan, *Analyst,* **86**, 530 (1961).

56. C. Feldman and R. K. Dhumwad, 6th Conference on Analytical Chemistry in Nuclear Reactors Chemical Technology, Gatlinburg, Tenn., 1963.

57. D. J. David, *Nature,* **187**, 1109 (1960).

58. D. J. David, *Analyst,* **86**, 730 (1961).

59. B. Belcher, *Anal. Chim. Acta,* **30**, 64 (1964).

60. D. J. David, *Analyst,* **87**, 576 (1962).

61. T. Takeuchi and M. Suzuki, *Talanta,* **11**, 1391 (1964).

62. J. B. Willis, *Spectrochim. Acta,* **16**, 551 (1960).

63. V. A. Fassel and V. G. Mossotti, *Anal. Chem.,* **35**, 252 (1963).

64. A. Strasheim and G. T. Wessels, *Appl. Spectry.,* **17**, 65 (1963).

65. S. Sprague, D. C. Manning, and W. Slavin, *Perkin-Elmer Corp. Newsletter, No. 20,* 1964.

66. R. Belcher, R. M. Dagnal, and T. S. West, *Talanta,* **11**, 1257 (1964).

67. B. S. Rawlings and M. C. Greaves, *Nature,* **188**, 137 (1960).

68. B. S. Rawlings, M. D. Amos, and M. C. Greaves, *Australasian Inst. Mining & Met. Proc.,* **1961**, 199.

69. L. Wilson, *Anal. Chim. Acta,* **30**, 377 (1964).

70. L. Wilson, *Anal. Chim. Acta,* **30**, 377 (1964).

71. J. W. Robinson, *Anal. Chim. Acta,* **23**, 458 (1960).

72. J. Perkins, *Analyst,* **88**, 324 (1963).

73. E. J. Aggazi, *Anal. Chem.,* **37**, 365 (1965).

74. W. Slavin and D. C. Manning, *Anal. Chem.,* **35**, 253 (1963).

75. V. Fassel, private communication, 1962.

76. T. L. Chang, T. A. Gover, and W. H. Harrison, *Anal. Chim. Acta,* in press.

77. J. A. F. Gidley and J. T. Jones, *Analyst,* **1960**, 249.

78. H. E. Parker, *Perkin-Elmer Newsletter, No. 13,* May 1963.

CHAPTER FIVE

Topics Related to Atomic Absorption: Oscillator Strength, Vacuum Ultraviolet, and Atomic Fluorescence

I. DETERMINATION OF f, THE OSCILLATOR STRENGTH, BY ATOMIC ABSORPTION

The degree of absorption by a resonance line as given by Equation (5.1) is

$$\int K\nu \, d\nu = \frac{\pi e^2}{mc} Nf \qquad (5.1)$$

The symbols have the same meaning as indicated in Chapter 1, Section I. The variables in this equation are $K\nu$, $d\nu$, N, and f. These are all interdependent and have the relationship indicated by Equation (5.1) as

$$\int K\nu \, d\nu = \text{const} \times Nf$$

The term $\int K\nu \, d\nu$ can be determined as the amount of light of wave number ν that is absorbed by a given population of atoms. N is the number of atoms in this population and f is the oscillator strength of the absorbing line.

The amount of light absorbed is equal to the product of N, f, and a calculable constant. If N is measured, then f can be calculated, or if f is known from other work, then N can be calculated.

This reasoning originally suggested by Walsh (1) has been applied very successfully by Vidale of the General Electric Co., who in an initial paper (2) on this work used a chilled sodium hollow cathode source and measured the absorption by sodium vapor. The absorption wavelength was 5890 A. The oscillator strength of this line had been previously determined. From these two pieces of information, he calculated N, the number of sodium atoms in the light path. This enabled a calculation to be made of the vapor pressure of sodium in glass at elevated temperatures.

In a second paper (3), he determined the oscillator strength of copper 3247 A resonance line.

A schematic diagram of the equipment is shown in Figure 5.1. The cell used to generate copper vapor is shown in Figure 5.2. The quartz tube was heated externally to a constant temperature, and the temperature of the copper

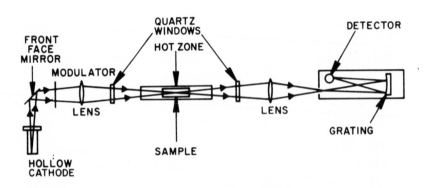

FIGURE 5.1

Vidale's Equipment for Sodium Studies.

cell was measured with a thermocouple. A slight pressure of argon was maintained to prevent rapid diffusion of the copper cloud. When steady conditions were obtained, I/I_0 was measured and f was calculated. Corrections were made for the shape of the absorption line as follows:

$$k_0 = \left(\frac{\pi M}{2RT}\right)^{1/2} \frac{e^2}{m\nu_0} Nf \tag{5.2}$$

where k_0 = absorption coefficient at the center of the absorption lines, M = molecular weight of absorbing species (Cu = 63), and $\nu_0 = 30784$ cm^{-1}, and

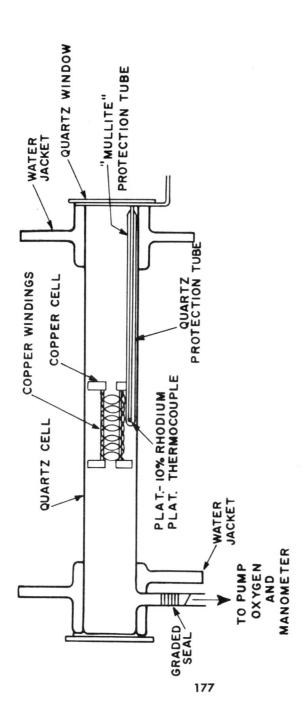

WATER JACKET

QUARTZ WINDOW

"MULLITE" PROTECTION TUBE

COPPER WINDINGS

COPPER CELL

QUARTZ CELL

QUARTZ PROTECTION TUBE

PLAT.- 10% RHODIUM PLAT. THERMOCOUPLE

WATER JACKET

GRADED SEAL

TO PUMP OXYGEN AND MANOMETER

177

FIGURE 5.2

Vidale Cell for Generating Copper-Metal Vapor.

$$k_0 = 8.512 \times 10^{15} \frac{P f M^{1/2}}{\nu_0 T^{3/2}} \tag{5.3}$$

The half width of the line is given by

$$\frac{\Delta \nu_D}{\nu_0} = 0.715 \times 10^{-6} (T/M)^{1/2} \tag{5.4}$$

where $\Delta \nu_D$ = Doppler width of the line and ν_0 = frequency at the line center. $\Delta \nu_D = 0.095$ cm^{-1} when $T = 1175°$K. By substituting the value into (5.3), we have

$$k_0 = 2.195 \times 10^{12} f P / T^{3/2} \tag{5.5}$$

A. Hyperfine Structure

The hyperfine structure of the resonance line depends on the number of isotopes and the nuclear spin of the atoms in the lower and upper transition states of the resonance line. On applying the selection roles for transitions $F = \pm 1, 0$ (F = the quantum number resulting from the combination of J, the electronic moment, and I, the nuclear spin), the relative intensity of each line can be calculated.

In the case of copper, the complete 3247-A line was found to consist of two groups of lines 0.04 A apart. This was beyond the resolving power of the instrument and was therefore ignored. However, two ground states were possible. The pressure of the copper in these two ground states was in the ratio 3:5. Let these be designated as state $'$ and state $''$. Hence

$$\frac{I}{I_0} = \frac{I' + I''}{I_0' + I_0''} = \tfrac{3}{8} \exp \left[-(\tfrac{3}{8} k_{(\nu = \nu_0)} + \tfrac{5}{8} k_{(\nu = \nu_0)} + 0.2) 1 \right]$$
$$+ \tfrac{5}{8} [-(\tfrac{5}{8} k_{(\nu = \nu_0)} + \tfrac{3}{8} k_{(\nu = \nu_0)} + 0.2) 1] \tag{5.6}$$

By rearranging and substituting Equation (5.5), we have

$$\frac{I}{I_0} = \frac{I' + I''}{I_0' + I_0''} = \tfrac{3}{8} \exp\left[-2.195 \times 10^{12} \frac{fP1}{T^{3/2}} \left(\frac{3}{8} \frac{k_{(\nu=\nu_0)}}{k_0}\right.\right.$$
$$+ \frac{5}{8} \frac{k_{(\nu=\nu_0)} + 0.200}{k_0}\right)\right] + \tfrac{5}{8} \exp\left[-2.195 \times 10^{12} \frac{fP1}{T^{3/2}}\right.$$
$$\left.\left(\frac{5}{8} \frac{k_{(\nu=\nu_0)}}{k_0} + \frac{3}{8} \frac{k_{(\nu=\nu_0)} + 0.200}{k_0}\right)\right] \quad (5.7)$$

The value $k_{(\nu=\nu_0)}$ is obtained by setting $\omega = 0$ in Equation (5.8) for selected values of a:

$$\frac{k_\nu}{k_0} = \frac{a}{\pi} \int_{-\infty}^{+\infty} \frac{e^{-y^2}\, dy}{a^2 + (\omega - y)^2} \quad (5.8)$$

The value of $k_{(\nu=\nu_0)} + 0.2/k_0$ was obtained by extrapolation on a computer. The value of P (vapor pressure) was taken from

$$10 \log_{10} P = 7.708 - 17.595/T$$
$$= 0.340 \log T$$

In Equation (5.7) all variables except I_1 and I_0 are calculable. By measuring I_1 and I_0 and substituting into (5.7), we can calculate f.

This procedure was proposed originally by Walsh (1), who suggested that f, the oscillator strength of a given absorption line, was a good guide to the analytical sensitivity when that line was used. He also suggested that solutions of salts of different metals could be aspirated into a flame atomizer, and the degree of absorption by the particular metal could then be measured. If the number of neutral atoms N produced in each case is equal, the relative oscillator strength of the two lines can be calculated. If two different metals are used, the number of neutral atoms produced may be approximately the same if experimental conditions are controlled, that is, by using the same sample feed rate, the same concentrations in the solutions. However, to get reasonable agreement, the energy to decompose the metal salts of the sample and the stability of the metal oxide formed in the flame must be similar. In many cases these conditions will hold and at least an approximation to the relative oscillator strengths can be obtained. Of course, if the oscillator strength of the absorption line of one of the two metals is known from other work, an approximate value of the oscillator strength of the second metal can be calculated.

The method can be used with more confidence for comparing the oscillator strength of two resonance lines of the same element. If the two lines originate at the same energy level, then N is identical in both cases. The relative or absolute values of f can be calculated as before, correcting only for the line shape of the absorption lines.

In a later paper (4) Russel *et al.* determined the oscillator strength of Cu 3247, Mg 2852, Na 5890, K 7665, and Cr 4254. The values they obtained were in reasonable agreement with those obtained by other means. They also obtained values for Zn 2138, Ag 3280, and Au 2428, which at that time had not been determined.

In similar studies L'vov (5) used a furnace for generating the metal atoms. This form of atomizer is free of many of the troubles encountered with flame atomizers. Chemical interferences and the loss of neutral atoms by oxide formation are virtually eliminated. However, after his studies he concluded that only αf for each element could be compared. Here α is the degree of dissociation of the metal compound and is proportional to N, the number of neutral atoms. He concluded that, if N was approximately equal for different elements, then f, the oscillator strengths of the absorption lines, could be compared. He further felt that even this approximation was only valid if the oscillator strength of the lines being compared were similar. In short his conclusions, even after using a much more refined atomizer, were similar to those reported earlier by Walsh.

II. ATOMIC ABSORPTION IN THE VACUUM ULTRAVIOLET

The region of the electromagnetic spectrum with wavelengths less than 2000 A but greater than the X-ray region is the vacuum ultraviolet region.

This region is so named because many gases, including oxygen, absorb strongly over wide bands at these wavelengths. Nitrogen also absorbs strongly at wavelengths less than 1850 A. Consequently, any studies carried out in this region must be carried out with no air in the light path. Preferably, a vacuum is used.

However, since nitrogen does not absorb at wavelengths above 1850 A, the ultraviolet range can be extended from 2000 to 1850 A by sweeping all the air from conventional equipment with nitrogen.

A number of elements have strong resonance in the vacuum ultraviolet. The majority of these lie in the region between 2000 and 1850 A. These lines should be usable with conventional equipment, if the light path can be swept out with nitrogen. However, flame atomizers would not be desirable, because it is anticipated that the combustion products would absorb strongly in these regions.

David reported (6) on this spectral region. He was able to detect arsenic at concentrations of 1 ppm at the wavelengths 1972, 1937, and 1890 A. Selenium was detected at 1961 A in concentrations of 0.5 ppm. Neither element was easily detected at higher wavelengths, and this information is potentially very useful. He also examined the absorption of mercury at the 1849 A resonance line; his results unexpectedly showed that mercury was not detectable at this wavelength.

However, work by Willis (7) indicated that mercury did absorb fairly strongly at this wavelength. He used a vacuum spectrophotometer and an oxyhydrogen flame. The use of acetylene or coal-gas fuels was impractical because the flames they formed absorbed strongly at this wavelength.

Sensitive results have been obtained in detecting As, Se, and Te in the vacuum ultraviolet range (8). It was found that absorption of the narrow absorption lines by the atmosphere was low enough so that it was unnecessary to evacuate the light path.

Other studies in the vacuum ultraviolet have been carried out by Nelson and Kuebler (9), who examined the absorption of phosphorus and sulfur.

III. ATOMIC FLUORESCENCE

Atomic fluorescence is a phenomenon similar in many respects to molecular ultraviolet fluorescence and is closely related to atomic absorption in the same way that molecular fluorescence is related to molecular ultraviolet absorption. In the process, an atom is excited by the absorption of radiant energy. The excited atom formed is deactivated by the emission of radiant energy at the same or lower frequency. This emitted radiant energy constitutes the fluorescence.

The fluorescent spectra of atoms is simple and corresponds to the transitions of an atom from one energy state to a lower energy state. In this respect it is similar to molecular fluorescence. However, in contrast to molecular fluorescence, the various electronic energy levels are not modified by vibrational and rotational states because simple atoms do not vibrate or rotate in the same sense that molecules do. As a result, the fluorescence consists of a few well-defined emission lines for each element. The frequency of these lines is characteristic of each element.

Qualitatively, the intensity of fluorescence is proportional to the following parameters: (1) the intensity of the radiation source, (2) the fraction of radiation absorbed by the atoms, (3) the efficiency of conversion of absorbed energy to fluorescence, and (4) the fraction of fluorescence self-absorbed by other sample atoms in the system. The fraction of radiation absorbed by the sample is dependent on the number of atoms in the sample cell. This fact allows the process to be used for analytical purposes.

The fraction of fluorescence self-absorbed by other sample atoms is also dependent on the number of atoms in the cell. At high concentrations this can be significant, and quenching of the fluorescence takes place as in molecular fluorescence.

A. Mathematical Relationships

Mathematical relationships have been adequately covered by Winefordner and Vickers (*10*). The following is based on their treatment.

The intensity of fluorescence is proportional to the quantity of radiant energy absorbed.

Therefore,

$$P_F = \phi P_{abs}. \tag{5.9}$$

where P_F = intensity of fluorescence (total)

P_{abs} = quantity of radiant energy absorbed

ϕ = quantum efficiency of the process, that is, the number of atoms that undergo observed fluorescence transformation per unit time divided by the number of atoms excited from state 1 per unit time

The relationship between the absorbed and the incident radiation is given by the expression

$$P_{abs} = P^0(1 - e^{-k_0 L}) \, \Delta \nu \quad \text{watts} \qquad (5.10)$$

where P^0 = intensity of incident radiation
k_0 = atomic absorption coefficient
L = length of the absorption cell
$\Delta \nu$ = half the base width of the absorption profile

If an absorption line is scanned from a point remote from the center of the line, absorption is zero. It increases to a maximum as the center of the line is approached. As the scan leaves the center of the line, the absorption diminishes to zero. The shape of the curve relating absorption and wavelength is the absorption profile of the line.

An approximation to $\Delta \nu$ can be made using the approach made by Willis (11). If the absorption profile is gaussian in shape, it can be approximated to a triangle. Under these circumstances, we have

$$\Delta \nu = \frac{\pi^{1/2}}{(\ln 2)^{1/2}} \, \Delta \nu_G \qquad (5.11)$$

where $\Delta \nu_G$ is the absorption line spectral width at half intensity of the gaussian curve. This quantity can be measured. By combining (5.9) and (5.10), we have

$$\begin{aligned} P_F &= \phi P_{abs} \\ &= \phi P^0 \, \Delta \nu (1 - e^{-k_0 L}) e^{-k_0 L/2} \cosh (k_0 L/2) \end{aligned} \qquad (5.12)$$

where $e^{-k_0 L/2} \cosh (k_0 L/2)$ is a correction term to accommodate self-absorption by the sample (12).

Equation (5.12) can be rewritten in terms of the intensity I_F by dividing P_F by the area A_F of the cell (a flame in this case) from which radiation is emitted and by 4π steradians. Then

$$I_F = \frac{\phi P_F \, \Delta\nu}{4\pi A_F} (1 - e^{-k_o L}) e^{-k_o L/2} \cosh (k_0 L/2) \qquad (5.13)$$

Equation (5.13) is valid only if the frequency of absorption is equal to the frequency of fluorescence, that is, for fluorescence from the first resonance line. If this is not so, the equation is refined to become

$$I_F = \frac{\phi_1}{4\pi A_F} \phi_2 \frac{\nu_1}{\nu_2} P_2{}^0 \, \Delta\nu_2 (1 - e^{-k_2{}^0 L}) e^{-k_1{}^0 L} \cosh (k_1{}^0 L/2) \qquad (5.14)$$

where ϕ_1 = quantum efficiency

ϕ_2 = number of atoms which reach excited state 1 per unit time, divided by the total number of atoms leaving state 2 per unit time

ν_1 = frequency of fluoresced radiation

ν_2 = frequency of absorbed radiation

$\phi_1\phi_2 \dfrac{\nu_1}{\nu_2}$ = energy efficiency of the process

k_{1^0} = absorption coefficient for fluoresced radiation (which may be self-absorbed)

k_{2^0} = absorption coefficient for the absorbed radiation

If several lines fluoresce, the term can be expanded further (10).

As in molecular fluorescence, I_F is proportional to N, the number of absorbing atoms. But as N increases, the term $(1 - e^{-k^0 L})$ approaches 1. Therefore, I_F goes through a maximum as N increases; then quenching begins and I_F decreases.

Where N is small, I_F/N is linear, and

$$I_F = \frac{\phi P^0 \, \Delta\nu k^0 L}{4\pi A_F} \qquad (5.15)$$

But early work by Mitchell and Zamansky (21) derived that

$$k^0 = \frac{(\ln 2)^{1/2}\lambda^2 g_1}{4\pi^{3/2}\,\Delta\nu_D g_2}\,N_0 A_t \delta \quad \text{cm}^{-1} \qquad (5.16)$$

where $\Delta\nu_D$ = Doppler half-width
g_1/g_2 = a priori statistical weights of atoms in states 1 and 2
A_t = transition probability
λ = wavelength of the absorbing line

By substituting (5.16) in (5.15), we have

$$I_F = \frac{(\ln 2)^{1/2}\phi\,\Delta\nu L\lambda^2 A_f \delta g_1}{16\pi^{5/2}A_F\,\Delta\nu_D g_2}\,P^0 N$$
$$= CP^0 N \qquad (5.17)$$

where C is a constant for any particular experimental arrangement. This leads to the relationship that the intensity of fluorescence is proportional to the incident radiation and the number of atoms which can absorb.

Many of the factors which affect atomic absorption will affect atomic fluorescence. This includes N, the number of atoms in the light path and f, the oscillator strength of the absorption line. All the factors which affect N in atomic absorption should affect N in atomic fluorescence in a similar fashion, and should include chemical interferences, solvent effects, atomization efficiency, flame composition, and the stability of the neutral atoms. These factors have been discussed in Chapter 3.

In contrast to atomic absorption, the degree of fluorescence of excited atoms should depend on the quantum efficiency of the process. This in turn is dependent on the efficiency of fluorescence, deactivation by other means (for example, collision), or the loss of radiant energy by other processes in the atom.

B. Advantages

The attractive features of atomic fluorescence include the following:

1. I_F, the fluorescence intensity, can be increased by increasing P^o, the incident radiation.

2. C [Equation (5.17)] can be increased by increasing L, the size of the flame, and the quantum efficiency.

3. N, the number of fluorescing atoms, is a function of the unexcited neutral atoms in the system. This is inherently higher than the number of thermally excited atoms.

4. A radiation source with wide spectral lines can be used.

5. The intensity of fluorescence is linearly related to the concentration of the sample element over a wide concentration range.

6. The element may be excited at one wavelength and the fluorescence measured at a different wavelength. This eliminates the effect of scattered radiation.

C. Limitations

The chief disadvantage is self-absorption of the fluorescence by the sample. This leads to a reversal of the slope of the curve relating I_F, the fluorescence intensity, and the analysis of the sample at high concentrations. It can be overcome by suitable dilution of the sample.

The limitations of atomic absorption also apply. If a flame atomizer is used, metals which form refractory oxides will be difficult to detect; also, with the present development of equipment, only one element at a time can be determined.

The intensity of fluorescence of a particular line can be affected by four types of fluorescence. Of these, sensitized

fluorescence in particular can cause a direct interference
to the intensity.

D. Equipment

The experimental set-up for atomic fluorescence is similar to that used in molecular fluorescence. In principle,
radiation from the source falls on the flame atomizer. The
sample atoms become excited and fluoresce. The intensity
of radiation is measured at right angles to the incident
radiation.

1. Radiation Sources

In contrast to atomic absorption, the radiation source
does not have to emit very narrow spectral lines. In atomic
absorption any unabsorbed radiation such as that from a
hydrogen lamp falls on the detector and seriously affects
the signal-to-background ratio. The loss of sensitivity which
would result has necessitated the use of hollow cathode
sources. In atomic fluorescence, the unabsorbed radiation
does not reach the detector and therefore has no deleterious
effect.

In an early work Winefordner and Staab (13) used Osram
lamps, mercury lamps, and electrode-discharge lamps. A
xenon lamp which emitted continuous radiation from 2300
to 20,000 A was also used as a source of radiation. However,
they were unsuccessful in detecting fluorescence from the
sample when this source was used.

In some of his early work Badger (14) used a carbon arc
as a radiation source. He was successful in obtaining intense fluorescence from Mg at 2852 A.

Hollow cathodes have been used in atomic-fluorescence

work (*15*). Although their narrow emission lines are an unnecessary refinement, this does not preclude them from use in this field. Further, because hollow cathodes are available for most metals, following the development of atomic absorption, they would seem the logical choice as a radiation source for this work. The high-intensity hollow cathode lamps recently developed by Walsh seem to be particularly attractive for this process because P^o is more intense and therefore I_F must be enhanced.

2. Atomizers

Flames have been used exclusively as the atomizer in atomic fluorescence thus far (*10, 13, 16, 17*). As discussed earlier, these atomizers are far from ideal. The efficiency of reducing the sample element to the atomic state is very low. Further, it is subject to numerous sources of error, such as chemical interference, solvent effects, the type of fuel and oxidant used, and the ratio of fuel and oxidant. However, these atomizers are cheap, convenient, and with a little care can provide reproducible and accurate results.

3. Detectors

The detector used by Winefordner (*10, 13*) was an RCA IP28. However, any of the detectors suitable for atomic absorption would no doubt be suitable for atomic fluorescence.

4. Modulation of Equipment

The bulk of the studies in atomic fluorescence has been made using unmodulated equipment (*10, 13, 15, 16*). This creates a serious problem when flame atomizers are used. The thermal emission from the sample element in the flame is frequently very intense and often much more intense than the fluorescent radiation.

Using unmodulated equipment, Robinson (15) was unable to detect sodium fluorescence at 5890 A because of the high intensity of the sodium emission. He obtained a similar result with nickel using the 3414-A line. Any fluorescence was swamped by the intense emission in the flame.

However, the thermal emission from Mg 2852 A was low compared to that from Ni or Na. He was able to detect fluorescence at this wavelength using a hollow cathode

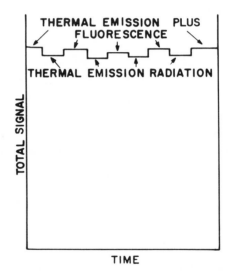

FIGURE 5.3

Mg 2852-A Thermal Emission and Fluorescence from an Oxyhydrogen Flame (18). The Fluorescence is the Difference between the Thermal Emission and the Total Emission with External Radiation Source Switched On.

radiation source. No attempt was made to optimize the signal. By switching the source on and off, a difference in total emission was observed. Figure 5.3 illustrates the intensity of thermal emission of Mg 2852 A in an oxyhydrogen flame, with and without fluorescence. It can be seen that the thermal emission is very high and the measurement of the fluorescence is difficult, particularly when it is recalled that thermal emission is subject to all the interferences encountered in flame photometry. Nevertheless, Winefordner and co-workers have been able to obtain very sensitive results in spite of these difficulties. Their procedure was to measure the fluorescence as the difference between the total radiation under fluorescent conditions, and the thermal emission under the same conditions, but with no incident radiation; that is,

$$I_F = \text{total radiation} - \text{flame emission}$$

Alkemade (*17*) overcame the problem of thermal radiation by modulating the source and tuning the detector. In the same way as in atomic absorption, the thermal emission from the flame was eliminated as a source of error. These sources of error include all those found in flame photometry, such as radiation from other atoms and flame combustion products. By using this excellent approach, he was able to measure the fluorescence of sodium as 0.25 per cent of the thermal emission under the conditions he used.

E. Analytical Parameters

Winefordner and Vickers (*10*) suggest that there are four types of fluorescence. These they define as follows.

1. *Resonance fluorescence* occurs when the absorption wavelength and the fluorescent wavelength are the same.

For all practical purposes, it refers to the use of the atomic resonance line associated with the transition between the ground state and the first excited state of the valence electron.

2. *Direct-line fluorescence* is a process in which the valence electron is excited from the ground state to a higher energy state. From this state it falls to a lower energy state which is not the ground state. In the process it fluoresces. The fluorescence is at a lower wavelength than the absorption wavelength. An illustration is shown in Figure 5.4.

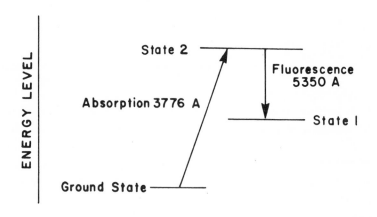

FIGURE 5.4

Direct-Line Fluorescence of Thallium.

3. *Stepwise fluorescence* is a process in which the valence electron is excited to a high-energy level. It then descends to a lower energy level without fluorescing, and from this level descends back to the ground state. During the final step it fluoresces. An example is shown in Figure 5.5.

4. *Sensitized fluorescence* takes place when an atom becomes excited and fluoresces in the normal way except that the excitation is brought about by collision between an unexcited atom and an excited atom of another species.

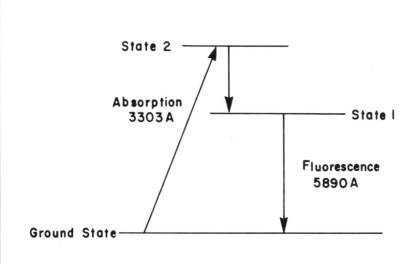

FIGURE 5.5

Stepwise Fluorescence of Sodium.

For example, in a mixture of mercury plus thallium vapor, the mercury atoms may be excited by irradiating the 2537-A Hg line. Excited mercury atoms collide with thallium atoms which in turn become excited in the process. Fluorescence of Tl 3776 and 5350 A has been observed (*10*).

5. *Flame profile.* Pringsheim (*18*) noted that when flame atomizers are used, the intensity of fluorescence varies in different parts of the flame. He found that there was no

fluorescence from the top of the flame and attributed this fact to quenching by hydrogen in the flame. A much more likely reason is that the number of neutral atoms is low at the top of the flame (see absorption profile, p. 64). In addition to the low atom population, it must also be pointed out that the hydrogen content at the top of the flame is very low, and therefore its quenching effect would be minor.

Nevertheless, it is still an observed fact that the extent of fluorescence is dependent on the part of the flame examined. Winefordner and others (*13, 16*) paid particular attention to this point in their studies of the phenomenon.

F. Analytical Results

The most serious attempts to use atomic fluorescence as an analytical tool have been made by Winefordner and co-workers (*10, 13, 16*) and by Alkemade (*17*). In 1960, after the observation of fluorescence of Mg 2852 A (*19*), consideration was given to the analytical potentials of atomic fluorescence. This was discussed with a major instrument company. It was decided that atomic fluorescence would be plagued with the problems of both atomic absorption and atomic emission. Since that time, the introduction of modulated equipment by Alkemade (*17*) and the experimentally demonstrated results of Winefordner *et al.* (*13, 16*) have gone a long way to proving that decision to be in error.

In their first experimental paper (*13*), Winefordner and Staab reported working curves for Zn 2139 A, Cd 2288 A, and Ag 2537 A. The general shape of the curves was similar to that shown in Figure 5.6.

Very little difference was found in the curve when the flame was switched from oxyhydrogen to oxyacetylene. This is in contrast to atomic absorption, where the type of flame used is very important to the results, particularly when elements like Al and Ti which have refractory oxides are examined. Perhaps later studies will show a closer tie, because the flame type affects the number of neutral atoms formed. This in turn affects absorption and should affect fluorescence similarly.

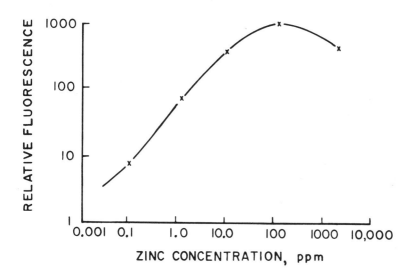

FIGURE 5.6

Relative Fluorescence of Zn 2139 A at Different Concentrations (*13*). Note Reversal of Zn Fluorescence in Concentrations Greater than 100 ppm.

It was found that organic solvents enhanced fluorescence. No doubt the mechanism is similar to that observed in atomic absorption (p. 76). However, one extra variable to be considered is the effect of flame temperature on quantum efficiency. This may increase at the higher temperatures obtained in flames when organic solvents are used. Since the intensity of fluorescence is directly proportional to quantum efficiency the former might be seriously affected when organic solvents are used. The results of Alkemade (17), however, indicated no change in the quantum efficiency of the sodium 5890-A line when the flame temperature was increased from 2000 to 2100°K. Further studies are necessary to clarify this issue.

Subsequently, Winefordner and Staab (20) reported the sensitivities given in Table 5.1. They were unable to detect fluorescence from the elements of Table 5.2.

TABLE 5.1

Element	Wavelength, A	Detection limit, ppm
Zinc	2139	0.005
	3076	1000.
Cadmium	2288	0.1
	3261	1000
Mercury	2537	0.1
Thallium	3776	1.0
	3530	1000

TABLE 5.2

Element	Wavelength, A		
Gallium	2874	4033	4072
Indium	3256	4102	4511
Selenium	2040	2591	

Further studies were made with refined equipment and a reducing flame (16), and results showed a significant improvement over previous work (20).

Detection limits were quoted as Zn, 0.001 ppm; Cd, 0.002 ppm; and Tl, 0.04 ppm. The detection limit was defined as that concentration which gives a fluorescence signal equal to 75 per cent of the noise level of the signal. It should be noted that this definition is in terms of noise level and should be compared to detection limits in atomic absorption, rather than to sensitivity limit, which is 1 per cent absorption.

Fluorescence was also found at the wavelength in Table 5.3. Further, they found that the intensity of fluorescence

TABLE 5.3

Element	Wavelength, A						
Thallium	5350	3519	2538	3530	2768	2580	2380
Gallium (10 ppm)	4172	4033	2874				
Indium (10 ppm)	4105	3256	3259	3039			

was linearly related to concentrations over the ranges:

Zinc	0.0001–10 ppm
Cadmium	0.0002–10
Mercury	0.1 –1000

These ranges are indeed impressive and indicate that the procedure holds great promise as an analytical tool.

G. Commercial Equipment

One commercial instrument is already available for performing analysis by atomic fluorescence. This is the Aztec Techtron AA3, which is illustrated in Figure 4.2. The atomic-fluorescence attachment is available for a moderate cost for use on this atomic-absorption instrument.

REFERENCES

1. A. Walsh, *Spectrochim. Acta,* **7,** 108 (1958).
2. G. L. Vidale, Space Science Lab., Aerospace Operation, General Electric T.I.S. Rep. R60SD330 (1961).
3. G. L. Vidale, Oscillator Strength of Cu3247 Line, General Electric T.I.S. Rep. R60SD331 (1960).
4. B. J. Russel, J. P. Shelton, and A. Walsh, *Spectrochim. Acta,* **8,** 317 (1957).
5. B. V. L'vov, *Spectrochim. Acta,* **17,** 761 (1961).
6. D. J. David, 4th Australian Spectroscopy Conference, 1964.
7. J. B. Willis, *Anal. Chem.* **34,** 614 (1962).
8. Jarrel Ash Co., Waltham, Mass., private communication, 1965.
9. L. S. Nelson and N. A. Kuebler, *Spectrochim. Acta,* **19,** 781 (1963).
10. J. D. Winefordner and T. J. Vickers, *Anal. Chem.,* **36,** 164 (1964).
11. J. B. Willis, *Australian J. Sci. Res.,* **A4,** 172 (1951).
12. A. C. Kolb and E. R. Streed, *J. Chem. Phys.,* **26,** 1872 (1952).
13. J. D. Winefordner and R. A. Staab, *Anal. Chem.,* **36,** 165 (1964).
14. R. M. Badger, *Z. Physik.,* **55,** 56 (1929).
15. J. W. Robinson, *Anal. Chim. Acta,* **24,** 451 (1961).
16. J. M. Mansfield, C. Veillon, and J. D. Winefordner, *Anal. Chem.,* in press.
17. C. T. J. Alkemade, International Conference on Spectroscopy, College Park, Maryland, 1962.
18. P. Pringsheim, *Fluorescence and Phosphorescence,* Wiley-Interscience, New York, 1949.
19. J. E. Allan, *Spectrochim. Acta,* **10,** 800 (1959).
20. J. D. Winefordner and R. A. Staab, *Anal. Chem.,* **36,** 1367 (1964).
21. A. C. G. Mitchell and M. W. Zamansky, *Resonance Radiation and Excited Atoms,* Cambridge Univ. Press, New York, 1961.

Author Index

Numbers in parentheses are reference numbers and indicate that an author's work is referred to although his name is not cited in the text. Numbers in italics show the page on which the complete reference is listed.

A

Aggazi, E. J., 154(73), 155(73), *173*
Alkemade, C. T. J., 189(17), 191, 194, 196, *198*
Allan, J. E., 112(8), 121(8), 124 (8, 31), 125(31), 126(31), 128(8), 129 (41), 130(41), 136(41, 54), 137 (41, 55), 138(41, 55), 140(8), 142 (8), 143(8), 144(55), 145(8), 147 (8), 151(55), 153(8), 158(55), 159 (55), *171, 172*, 194, *198*
Amos, M. D., 71(2), *103*, 110(3), 111(3), 112(3, 7), 115(7), 128(7), 139(7), 149(68), 153(7), 156(7), 157(7), 160(7), *171, 173*
Andrews, T. R., 135(49), 136(49), *172*

B

Badger, R. M., 188, *198*
Barras, R. C., 124(32), 125(38), 129 (32), 130(38), 141(38), *172*
Belcher, C. B., 135(50), 141(59), *172*
Belcher, R., 148(66), 149(66), *173*
Bothma, C. J. C., 127(39), 128(39), *172*
Bray, H. M., 135(50), *172*
Brech, F., 125(37), 130(37), *172*
Brody, J. K., 39, *56*, 119(24), *171*
Butler, L. R. P., 19, 21, 26, *55*, 124 (30), 125(35), 126(30), 131(42), 132(35, 42), 158(35), 160(35), *172*

C

Chakrabarte, C. L., 111(6), *171*
Chang, T. L., 158(76), *173*
Clinton, O. E., 33, *55*
Coogan, C. K., 110(2), 143(2), *171*
Cooke, W. D., 24, *55*, 118(18), *171*

Crosswhite, H. M., 18(3), *55*

D

Dagnal, R. M., 131(43), 132, 148 (66), 149(66), *172, 173*
David, D. J., 113(10), 118(17), 119 (17, 21), 120(21), 135(21), 136 (21), 138(10), 139(57, 58), 140 (58), 142(60), 144(21), 147(10), 151(21), 152(57, 60), 153(60), *171, 172, 173*, 181, *198*
Dawson, J. B., 135(53), 136(53), *172*
Devaney, J. C., 125(37), 130(37), *172*
Dhumwad, R. K., 138(56), *172*
Dieke, G. H., 18(3), *55*
Dowling, F. B., 111(6), *171*

E

Elwell, W. T., 117(15), 124(15), 125 (15), 132(15, 44), 133(15), 137 (15), 158(15), 160(15), *171, 172*

F

Fassel, V. A., 145(63), 147(63), 156 (75), 157(63), *173*
Feast, E. C., 127(39), 128(39), *172*
Feldman, C., 20, *55*, 94, *103*, 112 (9), 115(9), 117(9), 124(9), 131 (9), 134(9), 136(9), 138(56), 140 (9), 152(9), 153(9), 157(9), 161, 169(9), *171, 172*
Fry, S. W., 119(23), 125(23), 129 (23), 144(23), 151(23), *171*
Fuwa, K., 82(7), 94, *103*, 117(14), 123(14), 124(14), 134(14), 140 (14), 157(14), 169(14), *171, 172*

Shelton, J. P., 54(23), *56*, 180(4),
198
Slade, S., 85(8), *103*, 121(27), 122
(27), *172*
Slavin, W., 132(46), 148(65), 155
(74), 156(74), *172, 173*
Sprague, S., 148(65), *173*
Staab, R. A., 188, 189(13), 194(13),
195(13), 196(20), *198*
Strasheim, A., 19, 21, 26, *55*, 124
(30), 126(30), 131(42), 132(42),
145(64), *172, 173*
Streed, E. R., 184(12), *198*
Strelow, F. W. E., 124(30), 126(30),
127(39), 128(39), *172*
Suzuki, M., 119(25), 144(61), 150
(61), *171, 173*

T

Takeuchi, T., 119(25), 144(61), 150
(61), *171, 173*
Thomas, P. E., 110(3), 111(3), 112
(3), *171*

V

Vallee, B. L., 82(7), 94, *103*, 117
(14), 123(14), 124(14), 134(14),
140(14), 157(14), 169(14), *171,
172*
Van Zyl, C. R., 127(39), 128(39),
172
Veillon, C., 189(16), 194(16), 196
(16), *198*
Vickers, T. J., 183, 185(10), 189
(10), 191, 193(10), 194(10), *198*
Vidale, G. L., 42, *56*, 175(2, 3), *198*

W

Wallace, F. J., 135(48), *172*
Walsh, A., 15, 19, 21(2), 28, 36, 37,
38(15), 54(23), *55, 56*, 110(2), 111,
143(2), *171*, 175, 179, 180(4), *198*
Wessels, G. T., 145(64), *173*
West, T. S., 131(43), 132, 148(66),
149(66), *172, 173*
Whittington, C. M., 125(36), 141
(36), 158(36), *172*
Willis, J. B., 115(12), 116(13), 117
(12, 13), 118(12, 13, 19, 20), 120
(12, 19, 20), 121, 123(12), 125(33,
36), 126(12), 127(12), 131(12),
132(13), 133(12), 134(12), 135(19,
51, 52), 136(19, 51), 138(13), 139
(13), 141(13, 36), 143(12), 144
(19, 62), 148(12), 151(62), 152
(12), 157(12), 158(13, 36), 159
(13), 161, *171, 172, 173*, 182, 184,
198
Wilmhurst, J. K., 110(2), 143(2),
171
Wilson, L., 149(69, 70), *173*
Winefordner, J. D., 183, 185(10),
188, 189(10, 13, 16), 191, 193(10),
194, 195(13), 196(16, 20), *198*

Y

Yokoyama, Y., 72(3), *103*, 134(47),
172

Z

Zamansky, M. W., 186, *198*
Zeeman, P. B., 125(35), 158(35),
160(35), *172*

Subject Index

A

Absorption, coefficient, 176
    profile, 184
    relationship, 5
    signal, 3, 57
    wavelength, 52, 58, 61
Accuracy, 7
Acetone, 82, 91
Alkaline earth carbonates, 114, 152
Aluminum, 39, 40, 71, 73, 106, 110, 118
    alloys, 123, 135, 149, 158
Amyl acetate, 91
Animal tissue, 118, 119, 135, 158
Anions, 66, 75
Antimony, 106, 112
Arsenic, 106, 113, 181, 182
Atom, population, 3, 4, 6, 58, 67, 82, 83, 85
    stability, 65
Atomic fluorescence, 163, 182
Atomizers, 29, 62, 63
Aztec instrument, 161, 162, 197

B

Barium, 106, 113
Beckman instrument, 163
Beer, 118, 124, 129, 144, 151
Beer-Lambert law, 5
Benzene, 91
Beryllium, 39, 71, 106, 114, 118
Bismuth, 106
Blood, plasma, 121, 137, 139
    serum, 118, 119, 125, 135, 144, 151
Bone ash, 119, 135, 144, 151
Boron, 42, 71, 106, 116
Burner, design, 67
    Lundegardh, 32
    mechanical, 34, 86
    total consumption, 30, 32
Butter, 124

C

Cadmium, 106, 194, 196, 197
Calcium, 39, 73, 106, 118
Calibration curves, 7
Carbon arc, 188
Carbon tetrachloride, 91
Carbonate, 75
Cast iron, 135
Cations, 72
Cement, 118, 129, 135, 144
Cesium, 106, 120
Chemical interferences, 7, 8, 10, 67, 74, 75, 98, 102, 189
Chloride, 75
Chromium, 69, 75, 106, 121, 180
Cobalt, 106, 123
Commercial equipment, 160
Continuous radiation sources, 24
Copper, 42, 62, 106, 108, 124, 148, 176, 178, 180
    alloys, 123, 132, 137, 148, 154, 158
    ores, 123
Crude oils, 124
Cyanide waste, 128
Cyclohexane, 91

D

Demountable hollow cathode, 20
Detectors, 14, 47
Direct-line fluorescence, 192
Discharge lamp, 24
Dispersion, 98
Doppler effect, 13, 16, 26
Double-beam system, 51
Dysprosium, 42

E

EDTA, 76, 102, 118, 135
Electrical discharge atomizers, 39
Electroplating solutions, 124, 129, 141, 158
Emission signal, 3, 8, 76
Ethyl acetate, 91
Ethyl alcohol, 91
Europium, 42
Excitation, energy, 4
    interferences, 98, 99
Excited atom, lifetime, 64
    population, 4

F

Fecal materials, 135
Fertilizers, 123, 129, 137, 139, 158
Flame, absorption, 77, 79, 80, 81
    atomizer, 10, 30, 63, 189
    composition, 65, 70